STEPPING UP®
A CALL TO COURAGEOUS MANHOOD
BASED ON THE BOOK BY DENNIS RAINEY

WRITTEN BY
TIM GRISSOM AND JOHN MAJORS

FamilyLife Publishing®
Little Rock, Arkansas

Stepping Up: A Call to Courageous Manhood
Video Series Workbook

FamilyLife Publishing®
5800 Ranch Drive
Little Rock, Arkansas 72223
1-800-FL-TODAY • FamilyLife.com
FLTI, d/b/a FamilyLife®, is a ministry of Cru®

Video series workbook written by Tim Grissom and John Majors

ISBN: 978-1-60200-786-4

© 2012 FamilyLife

Design: Brand Navigation, LLC
Photography: iStockphoto and BigStock

Printed in the United States of America

21 20 19 18 17   1 2 3 4 5

FAMILYLIFE®

We become just by doing things that are just,
temperate by doing things that are temperate, and
courageous by doing things that are courageous.

—ARISTOTLE

CONTENTS

HOW TO USE THIS WORKBOOK

You hear it all the time: "Men don't like to read." Really? Then why have many of the world's most historic libraries been built and collected by men? Why are so many authors men? We're not buying it anymore. Men like to read, but they don't like to be bored. So we've tried to design this workbook to appeal to a wide variety of guys, both those who just want to "git-r-done," and those who want to linger a while.

The goal here is to help you understand the five steps of manhood, the progression that occurs across those steps, and then to help you build a personalized action plan for "stepping up" in one key area of your life. Our hope is that this will be done in the context of a "band of brothers," a group of men who'll share their stories and thoughts while sharpening one another.

To accomplish this, each chapter has four main components:

1. **Group Discussion questions:** We call it "Gathering at Base Camp." This is a series of questions to help a group of men process the content of the video sessions and the workbook.

2. **Personal Exercise:** This is where you'll be "Logging Time on the Trail" (clever, huh?). These exercises, three days' worth each week, will help you personalize the content from the videos and help you build an action plan that will be finalized at the end of the series.

3. **Stepping Up Plan:** You'll capture a few key things from each session at the end of day 3. These will make up the bigger parts of your Stepping Up Plan (which we describe below).

4. **A Step Beyond:** These sections are for the guy who wants to go a little deeper. Additional readings from Dennis Rainey's book are also cited to give you more to chew on. If you plan to work through these sections, you'll want to also pick up a copy of the book *Stepping Up*.

THE STEPPING UP PLAN (SUP)

All the information you are processing over the course of this series is designed to help you come away with one or two key actions you can take to continue progressing in your journey as a man. Even though you will be capturing lots of ideas, our goal is to simplify everything and help you come away with one big action item that we call the "next step". You're most likely to take action if you target one action (think rifle) rather than shoot and hope (think shotgun) over a whole host of ideas. Not that we have anything against shotguns.

The Stepping Up Plan is the foldout that is found in the back of this workbook. Throughout the course of the study you'll be transferring information to it. Near the end of the series (session 10), you'll use the work you've done in all the previous sessions to develop an action plan for taking your next step—the one thing you need to do to keep "stepping up" to manhood.

ONE FINAL THOUGHT

As you work through these sessions, do your best to move quickly through the material to avoid bogging down on any one question. Of course, if you feel the need to linger and dig deeper on any one issue, by all means, set up camp. But also feel the freedom to move quickly toward the goal. The main thing is to keep moving to make sure you allow time to identify items for your Stepping Up Plan.

Also, we recognize there is quite a bit of hunting-fishing-outdoors type of manhood talk going on in this series. We know that the essence of manhood is not wrapped up in the way you handle a firearm or a fishing pole, and that not every guy cares to go tromping through poison ivy. Be encouraged that we've done our best to also appeal to the indoor at heart, to the man who bravely conquers the heights of the office tower, with worn briefcase in tow, whose fingertips are callused, and whose coffee mug is respectably stained. The essence of manhood is more than a location; it is an attitude. So take heart and step in to this study knowing that the most important part is to come away with an action plan that fits the person God has made you to be.

FOREWORD

Gideon eased into manhood. At best he was an excuse-maker; at worst he was a coward. Until God turned him into a hero.

To be fair, Gideon was just one faint heart among many. His story is told in the Book of Judges.

"The people of Israel did what was evil in the sight of the LORD, and the LORD gave them into the hand of Midian seven years. And the hand of Midian overpowered Israel, and because of Midian the people of Israel made for themselves the dens that are in the mountains and the caves and the strongholds (6:1–2)."

Whenever their enemies showed up, the people of Israel ran for the hills to the safety of their prefab bunkers. This went on for years, and then God determined the time had come to deliver them. For that He needed a champion, a man who could rally the nation. Gideon was His man. But first, Gideon had to be coaxed out of hiding.

When God dispatched an angel to give Gideon the assignment, the angel found Gideon threshing wheat in a winepress (roughly translated: doing chores behind the barn for fear of his enemies). And then the angel greeted him in a way that would have been hilarious if it hadn't also been prophetic: "The LORD is with you, O mighty man of valor."

At the moment Gideon was not at all acting like a mighty man of valor. But in that greeting is a lesson for all men: God looks beyond the way *we are* all the way to what *we will become.* (Much like the way Jesus chose His disciples.)

Even after his calling, Gideon continued for a while to make excuses and question whether God had picked the right man. But God kept right on calling him, and training him, and using him. And somewhere, in the midst of *doing*, Gideon became courageous.

God probably isn't calling you to lead a nation into battle, but He does have work for you to do. And there's a chance that some of that work will require more than you feel you have to give. At first, you might make excuses . . . or question God . . . or hide in a bunker.

But listen. Can you hear it?

The LORD is with you, O mighty man of valor!

Dennis Rainey,
President and CEO of FamilyLife

A CALL TO COURAGE

GROUP DISCUSSION: GATHERING AT BASE CAMP

1. Who are some of the most courageous people you've known? What did you most admire about them?

2. How do you define courage?

3. Read 1 Corinthians 16:13–14 below, and explain how it relates to living courageously.

> Be watchful, stand firm in the faith, act like men, be strong. Let all that you do be done in love.

4.　In what ways do men need courage for daily living?

5.　What's the most courageous thing you've ever done?

PERSONAL EXERCISE: LOGGING TIME ON THE TRAIL

DAY ONE

DEFINING COURAGE

What is courage? Seems like a simple question. It's a common word, used in a wide variety of ways. For instance, men call war heroes courageous, but use the same word to describe a man changing a diaper, playing sports, or eating his mother-in-law's cooking. No doubt these are all different degrees of courage.

So what is courage, really? It's a question the video wrestled with and one we want to help you answer. Start by taking your own stab at it: What is courage, at its very core? How do you define courage?

1. Courage is:

Many well-known people have proposed definitions:

> Courage is being scared to death, and saddling up anyway.
>
> —JOHN WAYNE

> Courage is fear holding on a minute longer.
>
> —GEORGE S. PATTON

> Courage is . . . a strong desire to live taking the form of a readiness to die.
>
> —G. K. CHESTERTON

> Courage is not the absence of fear, but rather the judgment that something else is more important.
>
> —AMBROSE REDMOON

> Courage is knowing what not to fear.
>
> —PLATO

> Courage is doing what you're afraid to do. There can be no courage unless you're scared.
>
> —WORLD WAR I FLYING ACE EDDIE RICKENBACKER

It is interesting that fear stands front and center in each of these definitions. Courage almost always has a "nearly messed my pants" factor. It inherently involves overcoming fear to take action. Webster's dictionary even defines courage as a "mental or moral strength to venture, persevere, and withstand danger, *fear,* or difficulty."[1]

In the book *Stepping Up,* Dennis Rainey said,

> When you read books or watch documentaries about men who, like Red Erwin, were presented the highest award a soldier can receive—the Congressional Medal of Honor— you notice that the phrase most often repeated by these decorated warriors is, "I was just doing my duty." They don't consider themselves heroes. They just did their duty in the face of danger. They were scared, but they acted anyway.[2]

Simply put, courage is "doing your duty under fire." Courage involves action in the face of resistance, whether the resistance comes from within yourself or from some outside force.

2. Who are some of the most courageous people you know? List their names below.

3. What do you admire most about their lives? What aspect of their lives do you most want to emulate?

THE QUESTION

Dennis posed the question in the video: "What's the most courageous thing you've ever done?" Not an easy one to answer, but it's worth taking a shot.

4. What would you say is your greatest act of courage? What would be your defining courageous moment as a man?

5. If you are married, and if you dare, ask your wife what she thinks is the most courageous thing you've ever done. If you are single, ask your parents or a close friend.

Many men struggle with answering this question, especially in comparison to heroic stories like Red Erwin's. The only grenades most of us handle are full of paint or pesticide. Hardly the stuff of legends. But courage does not apply only to the epic stories of heroism. Doing your duty under fire also happens daily in dozens of seemingly small ways. It occurs with every little act to overcome the resistance to do the right thing.

In the days ahead we'll explore this more and identify some of the little acts of courage you are called to do. Tomorrow we turn to the Bible for more on defining courage.

> "In the world you have tribulation, but take courage; I have overcome the world."
> —**JOHN 16:33** NASB

DAY TWO

COURAGE IN THE BIBLE

The word *courage* occurs in the Bible thirty-nine times (ESV). Most uses appear in the Old Testament, and most have to do with battles and wars. But there are some other interesting contexts as well.

1. Look up the following verses and write some of the key words connected with courage in each of these passages.

> Deuteronomy 31:6
>
> Joshua 1:9
>
> 1 Chronicles 22:13
>
> 2 Chronicles 32:7

The key phrases here are "Be strong" and "Do not fear." Of particular note is that each of the above verses connects all three ideas: be strong, be courageous, and do not fear. The Bible clearly enforces the idea that to be a man of courage you must have strength, and you must put aside fear. But to what end? Yes, most of these verses are about battle, but what were they fighting for? A new set of fig leaves? A stash of replacement sandal straps? Maybe some cords for girding up those sagging loins?

2. Think back to the reasons they were called to be courageous. What were they protecting or honoring?

These battles were fought at the command of the one and only God, and for His glory and honor alone. The courage the men were called to display was first and foremost for the sake of the name of their God—not for patriotism or for personal esteem or even for the sake of their families; it was primarily to bring greater glory to God.

COURAGE IN THE NEW TESTAMENT

In the New Testament things take an interesting turn. The word *courage* occurs only six times. Why did the word take a hiatus when

Jesus appeared? Were the disciples only one-fifth as courageous as the patriarchs? The point is not to undermine courage in the New Testament, but to show a different emphasis of courage.

3. Look up the following verses. Try to identify the courageous act that is being performed and write it in the space that follows.

Mark 15:43

Acts 23:11

2 Corinthians 5:6–8

Philippians 1:20

4. What would you conclude about courage in the New Testament that is different from the bulk of what occurs in the Old Testament?

5. What are the similarities?

In these New Testament passages, men were called to take courageous steps to testify about Jesus, to spread the message of His work and life. Some were called to risk their lives (Paul), some their reputations (Joseph of Arimathea). Though the setting is different from the Old Testament, the goal was the same: be willing to perform acts of courage for the sake of God's glory.

6. In what ways are men called to act courageously on behalf of God's honor today?

7. Can you name a circumstance in your life where you courageously acted on behalf of God's honor? If so, describe what you did and why.

DAY THREE

One of the key scriptures for this series is 1 Corinthians 16:13–14: "Be watchful, stand firm in the faith, act like men, be strong. Let all that you do be done in love." This passage can be separated into five key phrases, each loaded with meaning.

1. Write a brief description of what you think each phrase means and why it is important for you.

 Be watchful

 Stand firm in the faith

 Act like men

 Be strong

 Let all that you do be done in love

2. Of these five phrases, which relates most to where you are in life right now? Describe why.

It's interesting that one of the directives Paul wrote to the church in Corinth was to "act like men." This is about as literal as you can translate the Greek wording (the language in which most of the New Testament was written). The same word is also used to speak of a person "conducting oneself in a courageous way."[3] The word inherently involves courage. A man is most manly when he is facing his fears, bowing up his chest, and acting courageously. If you were writing the same phrase today, you might say, "Be a man," or even, "Man up!"

Paul was telling the Corinthians to act like men because of what was occurring in the church: sexual immorality, bickering, division, and favoritism. Part of his role in the church was to call men up to act in accordance with the Scripture.

> Stepping into a challenging family situation is an act of courage. Foster dads, stepdads, and adoptive fathers have unique struggles to their roles, but stepping in offers a child guidance altering their life forever. Consider Joseph, the father (or is it *stepfather*) of Jesus, who stepped in to love and claim Jesus as his son. May God bless you for being, like Joseph, a hero by choice.
>
> —RON L. DEAL

3. Have you ever challenged a guy to "man up"? What were the circumstances? How did it turn out?

4. If you could take a mulligan in how you challenged him, how would you handle it differently now?

5. Think of someone you know who needs to "act like a man." If he were to come to you today and ask for advice, what would you tell him?

6. How could 1 Corinthians 16:13–14 be used to help guide him closer to the meaning of manhood?

MAN IN THE MIRROR

Now that we're doing pretty well giving others advice, let's turn to the mirror. If you were to ask, "Who's the manliest of them all?" and the answer came back *negatory, nyet, nein,* or *nada* for *numero uno,* what would you do? Consider what advice you would give yourself.

7. How would you tell yourself to "man up"?

8. Has anyone ever challenged you to "man up"? How did they challenge you and how did you respond?

THE NEXT STEP

One of the goals of this workbook is to help you develop a plan for "stepping up" in some key areas of your life, a plan for taking the next step. In order to do that, this book will guide you through identifying and capturing those thoughts in each session.

+9. Thinking about the theme of this session, in what one area do you need to be more courageous? Read the list below and check all that apply, or write in your own.

☐ Taking on a project   ☐ Getting in shape
☐ Confessing a sin pattern   ☐ Confronting someone
☐ Overcoming an addiction   ☐ Leading my family
☐ Making a tough decision   ☐ Ending a relationship
☐ Following through on   ☐ Finishing my work well
    a project   ☐ Showing up on time
☐ Coming clean   ☐ Following my dreams
☐ Other:

+10. What has been robbing you of courage or keeping you from showing courage in these areas?

☐ Fear of failing   ☐ Concern about what
☐ Apathy or passivity   others might think
☐ Lack of information   ☐ Wrong timing
☐ Seems too risky   ☐ The wishes of others
☐ Cowardice   ☐ Other:

11. What action can you take this week to display courage?

+12. Whom do you need to talk with about this, either to learn from them or to ask for advice, as well as their support and accountability?

+YOUR STEPPING UP PLAN

You probably noticed that some questions are preceded by a + symbol. Your answers to these particular questions will be used to develop your Stepping Up Plan (SUP), which can be found in the back of this workbook. Take out your SUP now and do the following:

1. Identify the area of your life where you most need to display courage (refer to your answer to question 9 in today's lesson). Transfer your answer to the Courage section on your SUP.

2. Name one individual whose courage you admire and with whom you would like to talk about developing more courage in your life (refer to question 12 in today's lesson). Write that name in the Courage section on your SUP.

3. What robs you of courage? You were asked that question today (question 10). Even if you checked more than one "courage robber," select the one that gives you the most trouble and write it in the Courage section on your SUP.

A STEP BEYOND

Supplemental Readings and Exercises for Session 1

COURAGE ROBBERS

There's a story in Greek mythology of a king named Sisyphus, the legendary founder of the city of Corinth. Sisyphus had a pride problem, and for this Zeus gave him a creative punishment: roll a boulder up a hill. No big deal, except that it was rigged so that each time he came close to the top, he would lose control and the boulder would roll back to the bottom. For all eternity he was banished to perform this beastly burden—always in sight of the goal, but never reaching it.

Men know in their hearts what it means to act courageously. They *know* what needs to be done, yet many never quite get there. Something steps in the way and that boulder goes rolling back to the bottom once again. Robbed of courage, they decide it's easier just to recline on the boulder in the valley and give up the fight.

Thankfully Zeus isn't hanging out at your house, waiting to trip you up, but there are plenty of reasons men are robbed of courage in our culture.

1. What are some of the main ways men are robbed of courage today?

2. Why do you think men are sometimes so easily taken off course by these courage robbers?

HISTORY OF STUMBLING

Some guys find they have struggled with doing the courageous thing all their lives because of decisions they made long ago. It may have started with one moment of cowardice on the playground or an act of bullying in the barroom.

3. As you think back over your life, do you find any uncourageous moments you wish you could do over? (No need to list them all, but you might capture one or two that really stand out.) Perhaps it will be appropriate to share them with the men in your group at some time.

4. As you look at those situations, are there any patterns? Is there anything you were consistently avoiding in those moments?

5. Look back at the advice you gave yourself (day 3, question 7). If you could go back to those moments where you avoided doing the courageous thing, what advice would you offer to yourself?

6. If you could boil it all down to one thing you need to do to get the courage boulder rolling all the way to the top of the hill, what would it be?

Congrats for getting through this exercise. It can be pretty painful to think back to failures. Who likes to remember those? Now it's time to move on; no need to self-loathe over past mistakes. You can't change the past. But the best thing about failures is the opportunity to learn from them. If you're not learning, then you're more likely to repeat the same mistake.

READ MORE ABOUT IT

In your *Stepping Up* book, read:

1. "Stepping up means owning up" (pages 6–8)
    What do you admire about Michael's display of courage?

2. "A North Star" (pages 24–25)
    Describe what you learn about courage from this passage.

THE FIVE STEPS
PART 1

BOYHOOD   AND ADOLESCENCE

GROUP DISCUSSION: GATHERING AT BASE CAMP

1. In what ways is it helpful to think of the journey of manhood as a series of steps or stages?

2. Name some of the men from your youth who taught you about manhood. What did they teach you (good or bad)?

3. Why are some boys and young men drawn into the gang lifestyle?

4. A boy naturally wants to become a man. He wants to grow up, yet why do some men seem to stay in the adolescent stage longer than they should, or step back into it?

5. What things did Gregg Harris do to help his boys navigate the adolescent years?

6. What are some important things a man can do to train his boys (or other boys he is around) to become men?

From Your Time on the Trail (session 1)

7. What area did you identify where you need to display more courage? (See question 9, page 11.)

8. What is it that robs you of courage in this particular area? (See question 10, page 11.)

PERSONAL EXERCISE: LOGGING TIME ON THE TRAIL

DAY ONE

THE FIVE STEPS

In his book *Stepping Up*, Dennis Rainey described the normal trajectory of a man's life in five steps or stages: boyhood, adolescence, manhood, mentor, and patriarch. This progression indicates not only the seasons of a man's life but also the increasing load of responsibility he carries as he ages. In fact, the difference between living responsibly or irresponsibly will define a man's life even more than his age does. We don't expect men to look like boys, and we shouldn't expect them to act like boys either.

1. In your own words, briefly describe each of the five steps in a man's life by completing the following statements:

    Boyhood is a time when:

    Adolescence is a time when:

    Manhood is a time when:

    Mentor is a time when:

    Patriarch is a time when:

The English poet John Donne wrote:

    No man is an island entire of itself; every man
    is a piece of the continent, a part of the main . . .

Romans 12:5 gives a similar description: "We, though many, are one body in Christ, and *individually members one of another*" (emphasis added). The meaning is simple: Our lives are connected; the way we live affects not only ourselves. No matter which of the five steps (of manhood) you find yourself on today, you are influenced by those ahead of and around you, and you are influencing those who are coming up behind.

2. List the names of a few men who are your most reliable and respectable influencers.

3. List the names of those who are looking to you for an example to follow.

BOYHOOD

The first step is boyhood, which Dennis Rainey describes as an age of exploration and discovery. For some, boyhood was an idyllic time of innocence and fun when even their worst behavior was more mischief than malice. Sadly, for others boyhood brings plenty of bad memories and few good ones. Either way, boyhood shapes us. Years later we find ourselves either attempting to build on what we gained during that time or trying to overcome what we lost or never had.

+4. Describe two or three boyhood memories that have had a lasting effect on you.

+5. Reflecting on your boyhood, name a couple of men who had the best influence on you.

6. If you could talk to these men today, what would you say to thank them for their influence on you?

7. Boys need to be taught and trained. List three to five "life principles" a boy should learn before he moves into his teen years.

8. Thinking of the boys who are growing up in your community right now, what dangers and risks do they face if they don't have men in their lives to influence and train them?

DAY TWO

ADOLESCENCE

1. Dennis Rainey described adolescence as an age of pushing and pulling. What do you think he meant by this description?

The transition from boyhood to adolescence is just as easily marked by changes in attitude as it is by the physical changes underway in a boy's body. He's growing whiskers *and* independence. Any debate over which is growing faster?

More than anything else, adolescence is a season of transition. A boy is on the way to becoming a man. But this can be, and often is, a turbulent time for the young man and his parents. A boy doesn't take one fluid upward step and *voilà!*, he's a man. Instead he bounces back and forth, erratically. There's a lot of confusion going on inside him and it will sometimes come out as belligerence.

During this time, he's not only testing the tide of manhood, wanting more respect and fewer boundaries, but he's also continuing to dangle his toes in the safe and familiar waters of boyhood. He wants to learn to drive and still get to play with LEGO toys.

2. At approximately what age do you think a boy moves into adolescence, and why?

3. At approximately what age does an adolescent move into manhood, and why?

+4. Describe what adolescence was like for you. What were some of the key and defining occasions that happened in your life then?

5. Describe some of the new expectations we have of a young man once he moves from boyhood into adolescence.

Unfortunately, people often have a negative outlook on preteens and teens, and young people can sense it. The unspoken, or sometimes spoken, message is: Go away! You annoy me. The hurt this brings sometimes causes young people to withdraw from the adults—parents, grandparents, older siblings, aunts and uncles, and family friends—whose good influence is greatly needed.

Perhaps this happened to you. If so, you can probably still feel the sting of it.

On the other hand, some adults seem to get it. They obviously know that an adolescent is an adult-in-the-making, and they lovingly step in to help train and encourage him on the way. They exude love, patience, and understanding.

+6. Did you have anyone like that in your life? List their names here.

7. Have you ever gone back to them and thanked them for their role in your life? If not, consider calling them or writing them a note. Return their encouragement with some of your own.

   If the person or people you'd like to thank have since died, you can still (1) thank God for them in prayer and (2) contact one of their surviving relatives and communicate your fond memories of their loved one.

Truett Cathy, founder of Chick-fil-A, wrote the book *It's Better to Build Boys Than Mend Men*. Without even opening it you know the book has a significant manhood message: start training and learning early. A boy needs to grow up with a keen awareness that God created him to be a man, a godly man. The sooner a boy gets this reality planted into his heart, the clearer his path to manhood will be.

DAY THREE

KEEP MOVING

In the book *Stepping Up*, Dennis Rainey wrote, "With each new generation, we have lowered our expectations for teenagers. Today most people in our culture believe that adolescence is a time when young men should have all kinds of freedom and fun. They are expected to rebel, experiment with risky choices, play games, look at pornography, have sex, and generally get into trouble. . . . We expect teenagers to continue acting like children."

Do you see the problem? Generally speaking, we don't expect our young men to advance, we expect them to revert. And that's the opposite of what should be happening. Or, to put it more bluntly, they're going in the wrong direction. Instead of stepping up, they're stepping down, and with few consequences other than a sympathetic nod.

1. Do you agree with this assessment? ☐ Yes ☐ No

If not, what is your feeling about the life stage of adolescence and what should happen in a young man's life during those years?

2. What is so appealing about adolescence that draws many men back to it repeatedly?

3. Have you ever struggled with reverting to adolescence?
☐ Yes ☐ No

Are there any areas in your life right now where you are acting and thinking like an adolescent instead of acting and thinking like a man?   ☐ Yes   ☐ No

What are those areas?

Philippians 2:3–4 addresses one of the key transitions that should take place during adolescence: "Do nothing from rivalry or conceit, but in humility count others more significant than yourselves. Let each of you look not only to his own interests, but also to the interests of others."

As a boy grows toward manhood he should begin to understand that real men serve. He should start shifting focus from himself to looking out for the good of others, seeking to put their needs ahead of his wants.

4. Take an honest look at your own life. How do you think you are doing at meeting the standard of Philippians 2:3–4?

What adjustments do you need to make?

5. List two or three key lessons a young man needs to learn along his way to becoming an honorable man.

+YOUR STEPPING UP PLAN

Take a few minutes to work more on your SUP by completing the following exercises.

1. Identify one defining event or circumstance that happened in your boyhood (refer to your answer to day 1, question 4). Transfer your answer to the Boyhood step on your SUP.

2. Identify one defining event or circumstance that happened during your adolescence (refer to your answer to day 2, question 4). Transfer your answer to the Adolescent step on your SUP.

3. Thinking of your boyhood and adolescence together, who or what had the greatest influence on you during that time? (This could be a repeat of one of your answers to the two questions above; your answer to day 2, question 6; or something you hadn't thought of before now.) After choosing, write your answer in the Adolescent step on your SUP.

A STEP BEYOND

GROWING UP

> When I was a child, I spoke like a child, I thought like a child, I reasoned like a child. When I became a man, I gave up childish ways. —1 CORINTHIANS 13:11

This verse points out two things that are true of every man:

1. Things will change about him and his perspective of his world as he gets older.

2. He will change things about himself and his world as he gets older.

Things Change

Many things in life are beyond your control. You will age, and your body will gripe about it. People will move away and pass away, and your heart will hurt over it. On the other hand, some of the changes in life will bring you joy, such as having children, adding grandchildren, and paying off your mortgage. The point is that life has a natural progression to it . . . yesterday/today/tomorrow; last year/this year/next year; past/present/future. However you choose to mark time, one thing that never changes is that things change. Accepting this truth is not meant to be an excuse for careless living; rather, it puts you in a realistic frame of mind to take on those things that you can—and should—change.

You Can Change Things

While the "child" in 1 Corinthians 13:11 became a "man" through the natural process of aging, he also grew up by choice ("I *gave up* childish ways"). He stopped doing the things he used to do as he willingly put aside childish behavior in favor of more grown-up ways. This is a simple and liberating truth: by the grace of God a man can always grow and change. Today doesn't have to be a repeat of yesterday. True, some changes are harder to make than others, but the possibility of change is still there.

1. As you grew up, what were some of the natural changes that occurred in your life—things you had no control over?

2. What changes have you made in your life, by your own choosing?

3. What changes do you feel you should make in your life?

THE BIG THREE

In 1 Corinthians 13:11, the apostle Paul specifically mentioned that he grew up in the way he spoke, thought, and reasoned. We shouldn't think of this list of three as being all of the ways in which a child needs to grow up into an adult, but they are worth considering.

Speak

4. What do you think it means to speak as a child, and how does that differ from the way an adult should speak?

5. Read James 3:1–12 for a description of the power of our spoken words. What changes, if any, do you need to make in the way you speak?

Think

Paul said that he also grew up in his thought life, meaning that the thoughts he entertained as a man were not the same as those he entertained when he was a boy. This is not referring to temptations, but to ideas and interests.

6. What outside influences most affect a boy's thought life?

7. What outside influences most affect a man's thought life?

8. What can you do to take your thoughts in a direction that is good and pleasing to God?

Reasoning takes the thinking process a few steps further. Reasoning is what we do with our thoughts; we reach conclusions and formulate plans. So, a person who entertains childish thoughts will reach childish conclusions, and a person who entertains mature thoughts will reach mature conclusions.

9. What about the way a child reasons is different from the way an adult reasons?

10. How do a person's age and life experience affect how he reasons?

11. Is it possible for an adult to think and reason like a child? If so, what might cause him to think and reason on such an immature level?

THE FIVE STEPS
PART 2

MANHOOD, MENTOR, AND PATRIARCH

GROUP DISCUSSION:
GATHERING AT BASE CAMP

1. How is manhood defined in our culture today?

2. Think back to the definition of manhood Robert Lewis shared. (See page 34 for an outline.) Which of his four points stood out to you and why?

3. In your opinion, when does a boy become a man?

4. When do you think you became a man?

5. What challenges do boys face during their transition to manhood?

6. Why do you think it's important for young men to have mentors in their lives as they mature into manhood?

7. Who are some people you consider to be patriarchs? What is it about them that you admire?

For Your Time on the Trail (session 2)

8. What were some of the key defining moments from your boyhood and adolescent years? (See question 4, page 19 and question 4, page 22.)

9. Who were some of the mentors in your life during those years? (See question 5, page 19 and question 6, page 22.)

10. What did they do in their role as a mentor that was particularly helpful for you?

PERSONAL EXERCISE: LOGGING TIME ON THE TRAIL

DAY ONE

MANHOOD

Defining manhood is no simple task. Cultures from time immemorial have set their own standards for moving into manhood. Jewish custom has it occurring at age thirteen, marked by the bar mitzvah. The American practice seems to set eighteen as the default age, but without any clear event to celebrate the transition (other than voting and signing up for military service).

But most men know that age is not an inherent identifier of manhood. There are plenty of "boys who shave in this world", and plenty of youth manning up in tough circumstances.

Men need help defining manhood, but where do they go for answers? Imagine that you were suddenly dropped on this planet with no prior understanding or definition of manhood. You begin consuming all you can of television, websites, newspapers, magazines, and movies to learn how to be a man.

1. What would you learn about the definition of manhood from these sources?

2. How do you define manhood?

During the video, Robert Lewis defined manhood using the acronym REAL. He said a REAL man does the following:

> Rejects passivity
> Expects God's greater reward
> Accepts responsibility
> Leads courageously

3. How does Robert's definition differ from what men would learn from popular culture?

4. Of those four aspects of manhood, which do you think men most need to understand and live out today?

Read these quotes on manhood:

> We need the iron qualities that go with true manhood. We need the positive virtues of resolution, of courage, of indomitable will, of power to do without shrinking the rough work that must always be done.
>
> —THEODORE ROOSEVELT

> This is the test of your manhood: how much is there left in you after you have lost everything outside of yourself?
>
> —ORISON SWETT MARDEN

> No man has ever risen to the real stature of spiritual manhood until he has found that it is finer to serve somebody else than it is to serve himself.
>
> —WOODROW WILSON

> A man must at times be hard as nails: willing to face up to the truth about himself, and about the woman he loves, refusing compromise when compromise is wrong. But he must also be tender. No weapon will breach the armor of a woman's resentment like tenderness.
>
> —ELISABETH ELLIOT

5. Which of these quotes most resonates with you personally? Why?

STRADDLING

Men today seem confused about manhood. In the previous session we discussed the adolescent stage and the tendency of some men to straddle the adolescent and manhood steps, keeping one foot on each. This makes it easier for them to dabble in both worlds without fully committing to either.

Socrates said, "The unexamined life is not worth living." He also said, "Know thyself." This is why identifying the "straddle issue" is critical to your manhood journey. Taking the time now to examine your life will help you battle temptation from a position of strength if and when the straddle issue presents itself.

+6. What issue would most likely cause you to step back down and straddle adolescence and manhood?

7. How strong of a pull does this straddle issue have on your life? Rate it 1 to 10 (1 being none at all and 10 being nearly impossible to resist).

    1   2   3   4   5   6   7   8   9   10

+8. What seems to trigger this issue even when you think you have it under control (perhaps a certain person, circumstance, or memory)?

DAY TWO

FIRM FOUNDATION

An important part of your journey as a man is the call to keep stepping up, to keep progressing through the steps of manhood. But it's not always easy to keep from stepping back down. Men need an outside source of strength to establish their steps.

The theme verses for this chapter, 2 Samuel 22:33–37, were written by David, one of the great men of the Bible:

> This God is my strong refuge and has made my way blameless. He made my feet like the feet of a deer and set me secure on the heights. He trains my hands for war, so that my arms can bend a bow of bronze. You have given me the shield of your salvation, and your gentleness made me great. You gave a wide place for my steps under me, and my feet did not slip.

What we have here is a song of David, written at the very end of his life. He was reflecting back on everything that happened, the good and the bad, and he wrote a song about it.

Much could be written about David. In fact, roughly four books of the Bible are dedicated to some aspect of his life. His poems and songs are also collected in Psalms, one of the most well-known and beloved books of the Bible.

A short summary of David's life shows him as a warrior, a leader, a king, a man of deep courage and conviction, and a man of character. He was a spiritual leader for the nation, a poet, a man in touch with his feelings, an emotional fellow, but a man who also struggled with sin. His accomplishments go from grandiose to grotesque. Some of the best-known stories of the Bible come from David's life, such as a grapple with Goliath and a betrayal with Bathsheba.

1. The first thing to note about these verses is the emphasis on the actions God takes. Write the things God does that are described in this passage.

2. Now write the action David took as described in this passage.

3. How many of God's actions are listed and how many of David's?

Isn't it interesting that the *only* action David took in this passage is the bending of a bow? And even then he gave all the credit to God's training in his life. Being at the end of life probably adds perspective, but it is still easy to take the credit for the successes in our lives and blame God for the failures.

4. Do you give God credit for the successes of your life?

☐ I try to always acknowledge Him; it's a reflex reaction.
☐ I do occasionally, but I have to be reminded.
☐ Honestly, I usually take the credit for myself.
☐ I've never really thought about it.

5. Imagine you were in the waning days of your life. The end is in sight, and you decide to copy David's example and commemorate your existence with a chorus. What words would you use to describe God's action in your life?

A WIDE PLACE

Of particular note is the last phrase in this passage: "You gave a wide place for my steps . . . my feet did not slip." When it comes to stepping up, ultimately our dependence is on God. He is the one who establishes our steps when everything below the waist feels shaky and unstable. Yes, we are called to work hard to fix problems in our lives, but we need God to give us a firm foundation to stand upon.

6. In what area of your life do you need Him to "make a wide place" for your steps?

DAY THREE

WHEN DOES A BOY BECOME A MAN?

Earlier we addressed the challenge a boy faces transitioning through adolescence and into manhood. Part of the challenge is having some clear definitions of what it means for a boy to become a man. First Corinthians 13:11 says, "When I became a man, I gave up childish ways."

1. What are some things a boy needs to give up in his quest to become a man?

2. While there are those things that a boy needs to give up to become a man, there are also things he needs to take on or acquire. In your opinion, what are some things that need to be true of a boy for him to be considered a man?

> When does a boy become a man? When his dad tells him he's one.
>
> —BURT REYNOLDS

+3. How did you know when you became a man? Were there any defining moments that signaled this transition in your life?

4. Who were the men that defined manhood for you, the manliest men you knew?

5. What was it about their manliness that you most desired to model?

MENTOR

The way a boy learns to be a man is from other men. There really is no other way. Sure, you can read books and watch educational films, but if men are not actively engaged in the lives of younger men, something will be missed in the process. This explains why mentoring is at the heart of manhood. As a man, you need mentors and you need to be a mentor. You need to be pouring your life into others, to help them grow and progress.

+6. Identify key mentors in your life, people who shaped who you are today.

7. What do you appreciate most about their influence in your life?

Mentoring is not a one-way street. The best mentoring relationships have a great balance of give-and-take, where both people are offering ideas and insights that energize the relationship. Mentoring can also take on different forms, both short term and long term. Sometimes a simple lunch conversation can be all you need to get some key ideas from a guy to launch you in the right direction. It doesn't always have to be a formal mentoring structure and relationship. In fact, sometimes your mentors can be distant relationally. As long as you are able to get ideas, encouragement, and insight from the individual, he will have an influence on your life. Of course, you also need mentors in your life who are close enough to help you see your blind spots and direct you in areas you might not be aware of.

8. In what ways could you currently benefit from a mentor?

9. Whom could you reach out to for help as a mentor?

PATRIARCH

+10. We'll spend more time looking at the patriarch step in session
10, but for now take a moment to think of men you consider to
be true patriarchs. Who comes to your mind?

11. What is it about these men, in character and action, that makes
you think of them as patriarchs?

12. What about their lives do you hope to emulate?

One of the primary aspects that sets a man apart as a patriarch is his
burden for the broader community, and even the world. He has a wide
influence and is engaged in activities that have the potential of
far-reaching and long-lasting impact.

13. When you think of your family, community, and world, what is
one area where you have a burden for making a lasting difference?

UP OR DOWN?

Do you know where you are on the five steps, and do you know which way you are headed? Are you stepping up or stepping down?

+14. Of the five steps (boyhood, adolescence, manhood, mentor, patriarch), which step would you place yourself on today?

+15. In which direction are you headed at this time?

□ Mostly up   □ Mostly down

An important aspect of making this journey as a man is calling others up with you as you progress upward. You need to be constantly thinking 180 degrees. Who is in front of you and who is behind you? Whom can you learn from and whom can you invest in?

+16. We already discussed mentors and helped you identify some key mentors in your life. Now take a moment to identify a few people you should be investing in more intentionally.

17. What are some things you can do to be more intentional to invest in the individuals you identified above? (Keep in mind that it doesn't have to be a huge thing; it could be as simple as scheduling lunch together or dropping them an encouraging e-mail.)

For stepdads, mentoring is a good word for the role that often works best. Occasionally a stepchild will allow you to be "father" but usually they view you like a coach or mentor. Don't worry about who you aren't to them; be the influence they'll allow you to be today and keep growing your relationship.

—RON L. DEAL

+YOUR STEPPING UP PLAN

Add the following information to your SUP.

1. Transfer your answer to day 3, question 3 to the Manhood step on your SUP.

2. Name one mentor in your life at the present time (refer to your answer to day 3, question 6). Transfer that name to the appropriate place on the mentor step of your SUP.

3. On day 3, question 14, you were asked which one of the five steps you are on right now (boyhood, adolescence, manhood, mentor, patriarch). Place a box around the name of that step on your SUP.

4. You were also asked which direction you are heading, up or down (see day 3, question 15). On your SUP, draw an arrow next to the step you're on, indicating the direction you're headed.

5. Who are the men you are mentoring, or perhaps feel that you should (refer to day 3, question 16)? List two or three of those individuals on the Mentor step on your SUP under "Mentees."

6. Can you think of a man who stands out to you as a patriarch (refer to day 3, question 10)? Write his name on the Patriarch step on your SUP.

7. On day 1, question 6, you were asked to identify the issue that would most likely cause you to step back down and straddle adolescence and manhood. Transfer your answer to your SUP under "Straddle Issue."

8. Finally, on day 1, question 8, you were asked about what seems to trigger this straddle issue. Transfer your answer to your SUP under "Erosion Issue."

A STEP BEYOND

Supplemental Readings and Exercises for Session 3

MEASURE OF SUCCESS

Part of being able to direct your life as a man is understanding where you want to go. Having a vision for your life will help give definition and clarity to everything you do on a daily basis.

1. When it comes to having a successful life, how do men typically define success?

2. What would define a successful life for you?

THE CHALLENGES WE FACE

No matter how you define it, when it comes to achieving success, many men never get there. Even when striving courageously, they are pulled off course or distracted from their goals by all sorts of issues in life. Most challenges to success can be placed in three categories: the world, the flesh, and the devil.

The World

Jesus reminded us, "In this world you will have trouble" (John 16:33, NIV). Paul also wrote that this world follows a course that pulls one away from Christ (Ephesians 2:1–3). We live in a fallen world that is infected with sin. This environment of sin is corrosive, even when we don't realize it. It is the smog-filled air we breathe, slowly decaying our lungs and bringing down acid rain on our cars. Drip by drip the enamel fades. But not all is doom and gloom, because Jesus also said "Take heart! I have overcome the world." No need to go defeatist, but be aware of the reality of the situation. You will have troubles.

The Flesh

"For the desires of the flesh are against the Spirit, and the desires of the Spirit are against the flesh" (Galatians 5:17). Our flesh, our natural tendency to ignore God when we don't feel like doing the right thing, tends to rear up at the worst moments. Like when someone cuts us off in traffic. Just when we thought we were sanctified, we start brainstorming a thousand ways to slash a tire at the next light. Yes, we're pretty good at blaming the world and the devil for a whole host of problems, but probably the flesh is at the center of a large majority of them. "But I say, walk by the Spirit, and you will not gratify the desires of the flesh" (Galatians 5:16).

The Devil

No doubt about it, the devil messes things up. He is the deceiver (Revelation 12:9), a liar (John 8:44), prowling about with a desire to destroy (1 Peter 5:8). Yet he is also given far too much credit for causing chaos. He isn't behind every stubbed toe, scrambled NCAA bracket, or flat tire. Sure, there may be a target on your back, but you may also be experiencing an excess of your own flesh.

For now, we just want you to have these categories in mind. As we start to identify more specific action points, you'll also want to identify the main challenges to these goals. It might help to think in terms of these categories when evaluating what is holding you back in pursuit of your dreams.

READ MORE ABOUT IT

Turn to pages 97–102 in *Stepping Up*, where you'll find the story of Ernest Shackleton's Antarctic expedition. It is a story of endurance, heroism, courage, and triumph over nature. The leadership Shackleton displayed calls forth some essential aspects of manhood. Read the account and then answer the following questions:

3. What were some of the keys to the survival of the expedition?

4. How would your team have fared if you were in charge of this expedition?

5. What about Shackleton's leadership would you like to emulate?

Shackleton's leadership, his efforts to keep his men alive, was a supreme act of love. And when it comes to living as men, one of our greatest calls in life is to love others well. This is an active living out of "Love your neighbor as yourself" (Matthew 22:39).

WHEN DOES A BOY BECOME A MAN?

DR. R. ALBERT MOHLER[1]

When does a boy become a man? The answer to this must go far beyond biology and chronological age. As defined in the Bible, manhood is a functional reality, demonstrated in a man's fulfillment of responsibility and leadership. With this in mind, let me suggest thirteen marks of biblical manhood.

1. Spiritual Maturity Sufficient to Lead a Wife and Children

The Bible is clear about a man's responsibility to exercise spiritual maturity and spiritual leadership. Of course, this spiritual maturity takes time to develop, and it is a gift of the Holy Spirit working within the life of the believer. The disciplines of the Christian life, including prayer and serious Bible study, are among the means God uses to mold a boy into a man and to bring spiritual maturity into the life of one who is charged to lead a wife and family.

A man must be ready to lead his wife and his children in a way that will honor God, demonstrate godliness, inculcate Christian character, and lead his family to desire Christ and to seek God's glory.

2. Personal Maturity Sufficient to Be a Responsible Husband and Father

Unless granted the gift of celibacy for gospel service, the Christian boy is to aim for marriage and fatherhood. Marriage is unparalleled in its effect on men, as it channels their energies and directs their responsibilities to the devoted covenant of marriage and the grace-filled civilization of the family. They must aspire to be the kind of man a Christian woman would gladly marry and children will trust, respect, and obey.

3. Economic Maturity Sufficient to Hold an Adult Job and Handle Money

A real man knows how to hold a job, handle money with responsibility, and take care of the needs of his wife and family. A failure to develop economic maturity means that young men often float from job to job, and take years to "find themselves" in terms of career and vocation. A Christian man understands the danger that comes from the love of money, and fulfills his responsibility as a Christian steward.

4. Physical Maturity Sufficient to Work and Protect a Family

A man must be ready to put his physical strength on the line to protect his wife and children and to fulfill his God-assigned tasks. A boy must be taught to channel his developing strength and emerging size into a self-consciousness of responsibility, recognizing that adult strength is to be combined with adult responsibility and true maturity.

5. Sexual Maturity Sufficient to Marry and Fulfill God's Purposes

Even as the society celebrates sex in every form and at every age, the true Christian man practices sexual integrity, avoiding pornography, fornication, all forms of sexual promiscuity, and corruption. He understands the danger of lust, but rejoices in the sexual capacity and reproductive power God has put within him, committing himself to find a wife, and to earn her love, trust, and admiration—and eventually to win her hand in marriage. The boy must understand, even as he travels through the road of puberty and an awakened sexuality, that he is accountable to God for his stewardship of this great gift.

6. Moral Maturity Sufficient to Lead as an Example of Righteousness

Stereotypical behavior on the part of young males is, in the main, marked by recklessness, irresponsibility, and worse.

The Christian man is to be an example to others, teaching by both precept and example. True moral education begins with a clear understanding of moral standards, but must move to the higher level of moral reasoning by which a young man learns how biblical principles are translated into godly living and how the moral challenges of his day must be met with the truths revealed in God's inerrant and infallible Word.

7. Ethical Maturity Sufficient to Make Responsible Decisions

To be a man is to make decisions. The indecisiveness of so many contemporary males is evidence of a stunted manhood. Of course, a man does not rush to a decision without thought, consideration, or care, but a man does put himself on the line in making a decision and making it stick. This requires an extension of moral responsibility into mature, ethical decision-making that brings glory to God, is faithful to God's Word, and is open to moral scrutiny.

8. Worldview Maturity Sufficient to Understand What Is Really Important

The absence of consistent biblical worldview thinking is a key mark of spiritual immaturity. A boy must learn how to translate Christian truth into genuine Christian thinking. He must learn how to defend biblical truth before his peers and in the public square, and he must acquire the ability to extend Christian thinking, based on biblical principles, to every arena of life.

9. Relational Maturity Sufficient to Understand and Respect Others

Individuals who lack the ability to relate to others are destined to fail at some of life's most significant challenges and will not fulfill some of their most important responsibilities and roles.

While a man is to demonstrate emotional strength, constancy, and steadfastness, he must be able to relate to his wife, his children, his peers, his colleagues, and a host of others in a way that demonstrates respect, understanding, and appropriate empathy.

10. Social Maturity Sufficient to Make a Contribution to Society

While the arena of the home is an essential and inescapable focus of a man's responsibility, he is also called out of the home into the workplace and the larger world as a witness, and as one who will make a contribution to the common good. God has created human beings as social creatures, and even though our ultimate citizenship is in heaven, we must also fulfill our citizenship on earth.

11. Verbal Maturity Sufficient to Communicate and Articulate as a Man

Though not all men will become public speakers, every man should have the ability to take his ground, frame his words, and make his case when truth is under fire and when belief and conviction must be translated into argument.

12. Character Maturity Sufficient to Demonstrate Courage Under Fire

In these days, biblical manhood requires great courage. The prevailing ideologies and worldviews of this age are inherently hostile to Christian truth and are corrosive to Christian faithfulness. It takes great courage for a boy to commit himself to sexual purity and for a man to devote himself unreservedly to his wife. It takes courage to maintain personal integrity in a world that devalues the truth, disparages God's Word, and promises self-fulfillment and happiness only through the assertion of undiluted personal autonomy.

A man's true confidence is rooted in the wells of courage, and courage is evidence of character. In the end, a man's character is revealed in the crucible of everyday challenges.

13. Biblical Maturity Sufficient to Lead at Some Level in the Church

A close look at many churches will reveal that a central problem is the lack of biblical maturity among the men of the congregation and a lack of biblical knowledge that leaves men ill equipped and completely unprepared to exercise spiritual leadership.

Boys must know their way around the biblical text, and feel at home in the study of God's Word. They must stand ready to take their place as leaders in the local church.

THE POWER
TO STEP UP

GROUP DISCUSSION:
GATHERING AT BASE CAMP

1. What actions do you think most men have regrets about?

2. Do you have any regrets, things you wish you would have done differently?

3. How did Ricky's outlook on life change after he met Jesus Christ?

4. In what ways can you relate with Ricky's story?

5. In what ways does knowing Christ help a man step up to real manhood?

6. If you know Christ, how has knowing Him changed the way you view manhood?

7. Ricky was inspired and encouraged through his friendship with Robert. Who has encouraged you and drawn you into a closer relationship with Jesus?

From Your Time on the Trail (session 3)

8. If you are willing, share about the "straddle issue" and "erosion issue" you identified. (See question 6, page 36 and question 8, page 44.)

9. Share anything significant you learned about the importance of mentoring.

PERSONAL EXERCISE: LOGGING TIME ON THE TRAIL

DAY ONE

Of all that makes up a man's life, nothing is more important than his beliefs. Belief feeds thought, thought develops attitude, attitude drives action, and action forms reputation. Belief is the root system, and if a man's root system is deficient, or nonexistent, everything else about him is in decay.

We believe that the most important decision a man will make—whether life takes him to the most lethal battlefields of the world or to a relative safety zone of health, wealth, and happiness—is to give his life to Jesus Christ. In other words, the most courageous thing a man will ever do is surrender, that is, surrender himself to God.

Life apart from God is less than futile and locked on a collision course with tragedy. Consider these scriptures:

> There is a way that seems right to a man, but its end is the way to death. (Proverbs 14:12)

> The wages of sin is death. (Romans 6:23)

The great problem everyone has is that sin separates us from God, and there's nothing we can do to close the gap. Though we may try to earn God's approval by working hard to become better people, we must understand that the problem of sin runs so deep that our best behavior cannot zero it out. We need a savior, a rescuer.

1. Why should we be concerned with the fact that our sin separates us from God?

2. What does the Scripture mean when it says "the wages of sin is death"?

> Before I could step up to true manhood, I had to decide what I truly believed.
>
> —DENNIS RAINEY

Jesus Christ is our rescuer! Through Him God has provided salvation. Jesus lived a holy life in perfect obedience to God and willingly died on a cross to pay the penalty for our sin. Then He proved that He is more powerful than sin or death by rising from the dead.

> I am the way, and the truth, and the life. No one comes to the Father except through me. (John 14:6)

> God shows his love for us in that while we were still sinners, Christ died for us. (Romans 5:8)

> The wages of sin is death, but the free gift of God is eternal life in Christ Jesus our Lord. (Romans 6:23)

The life, death, and resurrection of Jesus has provided the way—the one and only way—to establish a relationship with God.

3. Do you agree that we cannot rescue ourselves?

☐ Yes ☐ No

4. If anyone or anything other than Christ, who or what might people look to for salvation and spiritual meaning?

THE COURAGE TO SURRENDER

To be rescued we must give up every effort to save ourselves and put complete trust in Him whom God sent. This is surrender, not to an enemy but to a deliverer. It's an heroic emancipation, not a hostile takeover.

John 1:12 says, "But to all who did receive him [Christ], who believed in his name, he gave the right to become children of God." To "believe" means much more than mentally acknowledging that Christ is the Son of God. As an act of our will, we must place our faith and trust in Him and surrender our lives to Him.

Do you have the courage to surrender your life to God? Nothing you've done or will do in life matters more than this decision. You can turn to Christ, surrender your life to Him, and begin the adventure of allowing Jesus Christ to transform your life today. All you need to do is talk to Him in faith and tell Him what is stirring in your mind and heart. God is not so concerned with your words as He is with the attitude of your heart. Here is a suggested prayer to guide you:

Lord Jesus, I need You. Thank You for dying on the cross for my sins. I receive You as my Savior and Lord. Thank You for forgiving my sins and giving me eternal life. Make me the kind of person You want me to be. Amen.

+5. If you have been a Christian before today, briefly describe your conversion. (Think of the events, circumstances, scriptures, and people God used to introduce you to the gospel.)

CONDEMNATION IS GONE, BUT SIN ISN'T

For the believer, Romans 8:1 is one of the most treasured verses in the Bible: "There is therefore now no condemnation for those who are in Christ Jesus." Sin can no longer condemn us, but it's not going down without a fight.

First John 2:1 reads, "My little children, I am writing these things to you so that you may not sin. But if anyone does sin, we have an advocate with the Father, Jesus Christ the righteous."

Advocate, as the word is used here, refers to both an intercessor and a consoler—one who mediates and one who comforts and encourages. As our advocate, Christ takes up our cause and keeps us on the path of righteousness. Clearly, as this scripture recognizes, this doesn't mean we will never sin, but we can be assured that Christ's work will never be undone. Even though the enemy of our soul will often accuse and (attempt to) condemn us, Christ "always lives to make intercession" for us (Hebrews 7:25). He will never stand down!

6. As a follower of Christ, what should be your attitude toward your personal sin?

7. If sin can no longer condemn you, what can it do? What words would you use to describe the effects sin can have on the life of a Christian?

8. Close your time of study today by thanking Christ for being your rescuer and your advocate.

DAY TWO

Many people view the gospel—the biblical message of redemption through Christ alone—as something they move past once they become a Christian. Having put their faith in Christ for salvation, they seek a "deeper" doctrine that will help them grow spiritually. But there is a flaw in this way of thinking: the gospel never becomes irrelevant to a follower of Christ.

Romans 5:1–2 reads, "Therefore, since *we have been justified* by faith, we have peace with God through our Lord Jesus Christ. Through him we have also obtained access by faith into *this grace in which we stand,* and we rejoice in hope of the glory of God" (emphasis added). The faith that brings us to Christ for salvation is the same faith that keeps us standing, or continuing, in His grace day by day.

In his book *The Discipline of Grace,* Jerry Bridges said we should "preach the gospel to ourselves every day." He explained:

> [P]reaching the gospel to ourselves every day gives us hope, joy, and courage. The good news that our sins are forgiven because of Christ's death fills our hearts with joy, gives us courage to face the day, and offers us hope that God's favor will rest upon us, not because we are good, but because we are in Christ.[1]

The gospel has great significance to the Christian, and always will. Through the gospel we were convinced that we needed a Savior, and we were introduced to Him. By His great sacrifice, Christ removed the curse that sin held over us and secured our eternal home with God. To say that our future is bright is a serious understatement! Yet we face an uncertain number of days, or years, of life on planet Earth. These days will bring their share of ups and downs, sorrows and celebrations, and shocks and surprises. We may be out from under sin's curse, but for the foreseeable future, we live in its domain.

We need God . . . now. Today and every day.

1. In what ways do you need God on a daily basis? (Check all that apply and add others that come to mind.) I need Him to

   ☐ protect me from the power of sin

   ☐ give me wisdom

   ☐ deliver me from temptation

> The gospel is the announcement that God has reconciled us to Himself by sending His son Jesus to die as a substitute for our sins, and that all who repent and believe have eternal life in Him.
>
> —J. D. GREEAR

- ☐ keep me safe from evil

- ☐ transform my thinking

- ☐ help me think about life from an eternal perspective

- ☐ make me pure in heart

- ☐ help me forgive those who have wronged me

- ☐ empower me to love the difficult people in my life

- ☐ get me out from under my guilt, shame, and regrets

- ☐ other:

2. The gospel liberates us from the curse of sin. How does it liberate us from the power of sin on a daily basis?

3. Taking into account the current circumstances of your life, how does it affect you to know that you are "in Christ" and not on your own?

4. In what ways has the gospel of Jesus Christ continued to change your life, even if the process has been slow at times, since you became a Christian?

THE GOSPEL AT WORK IN YOU

Referring to the saving power of Christ, 2 Corinthians 3:18 says, "And we all, with unveiled face, beholding the glory of the Lord, are being transformed into the same image from one degree of glory to another." The expression "from one degree of glory to another," or "glory to glory" as some Bible translations read, describes the transforming effect that occurs in a believer's life over time (often referred to as *sanctification*). While sanctification is a work of God in our lives, we can—and should—put effort into nurturing its process. For example, we can

_____ read and study the Bible on a regular basis

_____ begin the habit of frequent prayer

_____ be watchful for opportunities to acknowledge the work of God and thank Him for it

_____ set aside a portion of our income to give to God's work

_____ make prayer and waiting a part of our decision-making process

_____ seek out opportunities to fellowship with other believers who are growing in their faith

_____ develop an attitude of worship

_____

_____

_____

_____

+5. Some people refer to these as "spiritual disciplines," and this is just the beginning of what could be a very long and helpful list. These are things we do in response to God's love and to grow toward spiritual maturity. Go back through the list and (1) place a checkmark next to those things you are doing on a regular basis, (2) place a star next to those things you are committed to start doing, and (3) add other spiritual habits you want to put into practice.

DAY THREE

As a follower of Christ, and as a man who wants to live with purpose and courage, be sure of two things:

1. God has work for you to do, and
2. God will finish what He started in you.

GOD HAS WORK FOR YOU TO DO

God puts the desire for spiritual activity and accomplishment into the heart of each of His children. That's not to say that everything we do is missionary work. But it does mean that if we aren't engaged at some level in purposes that are God-centered, we will experience spiritual sluggishness because we aren't being true to our redeemed nature. Ephesians 2:10 says that "we are his [God's] workmanship, created in Christ Jesus for good works, which God prepared beforehand, that we should walk in them."

> God's work does not make our effort unnecessary, but rather makes it effective.
>
> —JERRY BRIDGES

Your life purpose is centered on God and His purposes. He has things He wants to do through you. Are you giving any thought to this?

1. What areas of your life are affected by knowing God has work for you to do?

2. What are some of the ways you can go about determining the works God wants to do through you?

3. Are you in any way reluctant to find out what God wants to do through you? Describe why you're reluctant.

GOD WILL FINISH
WHAT HE STARTED

All men need to understand the importance of follow-through. Good intentions are meaningless if they're never put into action. It's one thing to make a promise, but another thing entirely to keep it. It's admirable to make a commitment, but it would be better not to make it than to make it and not fulfill it. Broken promises lead to broken hearts.

Of this we can be certain: God finishes what He starts. That's the tremendous promise of Philippians 1:6: "And I am sure of this, that he who began a good work in you will bring it to completion at the day of Jesus Christ." In other words, God will never disown you. He will never give up on you. He will never regret the price He paid to adopt you into His family. And He will never set aside the sanctifying process He began in you on the day of your salvation.

More than likely you will go through occasional times when God seems distant or you're losing your spiritual edge. In those seasons perhaps even your desire to grow in godliness will break down. But your feelings don't represent all that is true. God is still at work in you. In fact, many people will say that their times of deepest struggle became game-changers because of what they were forced to learn about God and life when put to the test. What was theory became belief. What was presumption became conviction. And they became new men. Because God finishes what He starts.

4. Describe some of the ways God has changed you since you became a Christian. (You may want to ask others about what changes they've observed in you.)

5. Describe some of the life-changing lessons you have learned through times of struggle. Are you able to see that God was working even then?

6. If you are in one of those challenging seasons of life right now, take a moment to pray. Ask God to shape your life through these circumstances, helping you to grow to become like Christ. Also, acknowledge that God is at work even when your feelings may question Him.

+YOUR STEPPING UP PLAN

Add the following information to your SUP.

1. On day 1, question 5, you were asked to describe your conversion. This may be quite a challenge, but try to reduce that description to one sentence and write it in the Faith section on your SUP.

2. Choose your three highest priority "spiritual disciplines" of those you identified on day 2, question 5. Enter those three in the Faith section on your SUP.

5

STANDING
FIRM

GROUP DISCUSSION: GATHERING AT BASE CAMP

1. Even though the tomb guards were given permission to take shelter during the hurricane, they chose not to leave their post. Why? What do you think you would have done?

2. What are some areas where men need to stand firm in today's culture? How are you feeling moved personally to stand firm?

3. How do guys get tripped up in their efforts to stand firm?

4. How does a man stay pure in his interactions online? What are some things you do to guard your heart in these types of situations?

5. Read Titus 2:7–8. One of the character qualities emphasized in this session is integrity. What does it mean to be a man of integrity?

What are some ways a man develops integrity?

From Your Time on the Trail (session 4)

6. Share about your conversion, the point in time when you came to know Christ. What were some of the most significant changes that occurred in your life as a result? (See question 5, page 58.)

7. Of the three spiritual disciplines you identified, which is most important for you and why? (See question 5, page 62.)

> Show yourself in all respects to be a model of good works, and in your teaching show integrity, dignity, and sound speech that cannot be condemned, so that an opponent may be put to shame, having nothing evil to say about us.
>
> **—TITUS 2:7–8**

PERSONAL EXERCISE: LOGGING TIME ON THE TRAIL

DAY ONE

WHAT DOES IT MEAN TO "STAND FIRM"?

Ephesians 6:10–11, 13 says, "Finally, be strong in the Lord and in the strength of his might. Put on the whole armor of God, that you may be able to stand against the schemes of the devil. . . . that you may be able to withstand in the evil day, and having done all, to stand firm."

The Bible puts great importance on being able to "stand firm" so that one can withstand the temptations of the evil one and the challenges of life.

1. In your mind, what does it mean to "stand firm"?

2. Whom have you known that does this well? What characterizes them? What are some words or phrases you would use to describe this person?

3. Part of knowing what it means to stand firm is understanding what it does not mean. What are some ways men wrongly understand standing firm? (Example: he is unwilling to consider the opinions or feelings of others.)

4. Are there some times when it is appropriate for a man not to stand firm, but instead to "stand down"?

Part of properly understanding the Bible is learning to balance two seemingly contradictory statements. For instance, some look at the life of Jesus and are confused when comparing His aggressive attitude with the Pharisees to His humble attitude toward the poor. How could the guy who whipped up on the money-changers in the temple courtyard turn around and willingly lay down His life? Makes no sense, right?

Biblical manhood is a study in tensions: firmly gentle, strong and tender, aggressively patient—the slamming together of two terms into intimate relationship that seem to have no future together.

Real men come to understand this. They come to understand that there is a time to stand firm and a time to stand down, and there is a way to stand firm that is honoring and biblical.

+5. Write a few areas where you feel you need to grow in your understanding of what it means to stand firm in a biblical way. (Perhaps this involves your life at work, how you relate to women, your family responsibilities, friendships, or your personal habits and lifestyle.)

READ MORE ABOUT IT

Turn to page 25 in the book *Stepping Up,* to the heading "Manly Men." Read this section and then answer the following questions:

6. What does it take for these men to move toward danger while others are running away?

7. How do they develop that kind of courage?

DAY TWO

EXAMINING TITUS 2:7-8

[7]Show yourself in all respects to be a model of good works, and in your teaching show integrity, dignity, [8]and sound speech that cannot be condemned, so that an opponent may be put to shame, having nothing evil to say about us.

1. The ability to stand firm requires strength and character, a posture of poise in the midst of passion. Look back through Titus 2:7–8 at some of the character qualities listed in this passage. What key words stand out to you? Why are these words important?

2. One of the ways a man stands firm is to be a man of rock-solid character, a man of integrity. What does it mean to be a man of integrity?

   At the root of the word *integrity* is the word *integer*, a whole number. It is not fragmented or separated; it is complete in itself. A man of integrity is whole; he is sound and not fragmented. He is the same person in public as he is in private.

+3. Whom do you know that you would consider a model of integrity?

4. The verb—the action—in this passage is the word *show*. Would this passage have the same importance if it only said "be" and not "show"? Why or why not?

5. What are the results of living out these verses? (Hint: look for what follows "so that" in verse 8.)

> Character and trustworthiness are critical first steps for stepdads because stepparents are often unfairly judged by stepchildren. Stepkids are evaluating whether they can entrust themselves to you; early on you won't get much grace, so round off the rough edges of your personality (e.g., harshness, quick temper, or anger). Show yourself worthy of respect so they won't have anything evil to say about you.
>
> —RON L. DEAL

6. We are to "show" ourselves as "a *model* of good works." When you think of the word model, what comes to mind?

7. A model of something is a type, or a picture, of something else, always pointing to the real thing. When you act as a "model of good works," what (or who) are you ultimately pointing people toward?

8. In what ways do you hope to show yourself a model of good works?

> For the grace of God has appeared, bringing salvation for all people.
>
> —TITUS 2:11

9. The ability to live this way is not necessarily natural. These verses are not just proposing some kind of mystical moralistic mosaic, as in, "Be good, Johnny, and you'll get a cookie." Instead, the power to live out verses 7 and 8 is found later on in verse 11. What does verse 11 say is the reason you can live out verses 7–8?

10. How does understanding verse 11 change the way you view the commands of verses 7–8?

11. Look back to yesterday's assignment to the areas you identified as needing to stand firm (page 71, question 5). How can Titus 2:11 help you in these areas?

+12. What steps can you take to become a man of integrity and a model of good works in these areas?

DAY 3

GET A GRIP

The Bible often uses imagery to make a point. A look at two examples related to standing firm might be helpful.

In Matthew 7, Jesus contrasted the wise man with the foolish, stating that the wise man built a house on the rock, while the foolish man built a house on the sand. Both houses were pounded by wind, rain, and flooding, but only the one built on the rock endured. The lesson? Wrong foundation, no security.

A second example can be found in Ephesians 4, where Paul likened spiritual immaturity to a vessel adrift at sea. Having no power supply of its own, the vessel is pushed to wherever the ocean current wants to take it. The lesson? Drive or be driven.

The root teaching in both Bible passages is that a man not anchored in Christ is unsteady. He's vulnerable, wishy-washy, and erratic. Other factors can cause him to act irresponsibly now and then, but a man whose life is defined by instability is a man who needs soul reformation. The fault line of character always runs through the spiritual life.

1. Identify the primary roles and responsibilities God has given you as a man. Check all that apply.

   ☐ Son   ☐ Father-in-law   ☐ Friend
   ☐ Brother   ☐ Employee   ☐ Neighbor
   ☐ Husband   ☐ Employer   ☐ Mentor
   ☐ Father   ☐ Boss/Supervisor ☐ Other:
   ☐ Grandfather   ☐ Citizen

2. Looking over the roles God has given you, think about the kind of job you've been doing in each area as far as standing firm is concerned. Give yourself a rating of 1 (weak) to 5 (strong) for each role. Are there areas or relationships that need some attention? Make note of those here.

GOOD STUBBORN VS. BAD STUBBORN

The concept of standing firm can be confusing. On one hand it sounds so noble because it appeals to our sense of rightness and to the masculine nature of guarding and protecting. The soldier in us will stand his post no matter how threatening the enemy.

You want to be this guy.

On the other hand, standing firm conjures up images of a self-appointed hero who's so convinced of his ideals that to him all other men are lesser men. He sees himself as the benchmark of integrity. He's enlightened, others are not.

You don't want to be this guy.

Both men are stubborn, one the good kind of stubborn and the other the bad kind. Look up the word *stubborn* in the dictionary and see for yourself the double-edged sword of its meaning: "persistent" (good) and "difficult" (bad); "justifiably unyielding" (good) and "unreasonably unyielding" (bad).

Good stubborn and bad stubborn.

3. Do you know a man who is the good kind of stubborn? What do you think of him?

4. Do you know a man who is the bad kind of stubborn? What do you think of him?

5. How do you think those closest to you—immediate family, friends, and coworkers—would generally describe you: good stubborn or bad stubborn?

6. How would you describe yourself: good stubborn or bad stubborn? List some areas where your good and bad stubborn come out.

7. If you described yourself as bad stubborn, what changes do you need to make?

FIGHTING ON THE WAY TO THE FIGHT

On the way to standing firm, expect to encounter three adversaries: fear, pride, and indifference.

FEAR

Depending on the issue you're dealing with, standing firm may require a new level of bravery. Sometimes the cost of facing life's challenges seems higher than we can pay. Second Timothy 1:7 tells us, "God gave us a spirit *not of fear* but of power and love and self-control" (emphasis added).

The presence of fear in our lives indicates a need for God. Sadly, many men ignore their fear, or try to overcome it on their own, and miss an opportunity to develop spiritually.

8. What causes you fear or anxiety?

9. What do you generally do to regain a sense of calm?

10. Do you make any effort to seek God during the times when you are anxious? How do you seek Him (for example, pray, talk to someone, take in the beauty of His creation)?

PRIDE

Many a man has been taken down not by the challenges he faced, but by his prideful response to them. Rather than opening himself to the possibility that he bears at least some fault in the matter, or that he could benefit from the insight and help of others, the proud man flies solo. And often crashes.

First Peter 5:6 exhorts: "Humble yourselves, therefore, under the mighty hand of God so that at the proper time he may exalt you [lift you up]." You may or may not have had any hand in your present difficulties, but you do have a choice in how you will handle them. Humbling yourself is an excellent place to start.

11. In what ways does pride complicate an already difficult situation?

12. The act or position of standing firm implies that there are forces trying to knock us down. Because this is true, we often need the help of others. Why is it difficult to help a proud person?

13. In what ways does a man's pride interfere with his asking for or accepting help?

14. Consider 1 Peter 5:6. How does a man go about humbling himself?

INDIFFERENCE

Men don't belong on the sidelines. There's too much at stake in our families and in our culture, and even in our own lives, to be a spectator. The simple fact that you exist, that God has brought you to life, means that He has work for you to do.

15. Read Ephesians 2:10. What are some of the "good works" for which God created you?

16. Standing firm means that a man cares enough to take initiative, to get involved. What people or causes move you to the point where you feel that you have to do something, that you cannot just let things go as they are?

17. How do you determine if this is something God wants you to do or if you're just acting on your own?

+YOUR STEPPING UP PLAN

Continue developing your SUP by completing the following exercises.

1. Identify one area in your life where you need to do a better job of standing firm. (Your answer to day 1, question 5 may help.) Write your answer in the Standing Firm section on your SUP.

2. What's the first step you feel you need to take in order to stand firm in the area you just identified (refer to day 2, question 12)? Add this step to the Standing Firm section on your SUP.

3. Whom could you talk to that could help you in this area? Perhaps a person that you listed in your answer to day 2, question 3. Write this person's name in the Standing Firm section on your SUP.

4. What is your primary "Erosion Issue" when it comes to having the courage to stand firm, the issue that holds you back from doing what you feel God wants you to do? After giving this some thought, write your answer in the Standing Firm section on your SUP.

Supplemental Readings and Exercises for Session 5

WHEN "STANDING FIRM" MEANS "TAKING A STAND"

Consider another aspect of what standing firm may require: taking a stand. Taking a stand means to publicly take a position for or against something. This could refer to any number of things—from headline issues, like human trafficking, to causes that are close to your heart because of personal experience, like foster care or adoption.

1.   List some of the issues or concerns that stir you to action, and briefly explain why each one is important to you.

2.   Have you ever regretted not taking a stand? What do you wish you would have done?

3.   Have you ever regretted taking a stand or the way in which you took a stand? What would you have done differently?

4.   Referring to the previous two questions, what have you learned from your past experiences?

Taking a stand usually means speaking out, and there is always a risk where talking is involved. Our mouths can get us into all kinds of trouble, especially when we're discussing or defending a position or person we care deeply about. Things said in the heat of the moment have generally not been thought through and may be received by the hearers as hurtful or demeaning. And while we can't control how others will respond to our words, we do have an obligation to communicate in ways that honor God, our ultimate audience.

5. When you talk, are you mindful that God is also present and listening? How does this awareness—or how should this awareness—influence your communication?

6. Describe some of the warnings and teachings the Bible offers about verbal communication.

One question is often raised: how do I know when to take a stand and when to let things go? This is not a cowardly question; it is a legitimate recognition that followers of Christ sometimes pick fights when they shouldn't.

Here is a short sample of the reasoning people sometimes use to determine whether or not to take a stand:

A. I feel strongly that I should, so it must be the right thing to do.

B. If I don't, nobody will.

C. I did before, so I must again.

D. People I'm close to think I should.

However, there is a common error in all four reasons: none of these include asking God what He wants you to do. That's not to say that these reasons can't play some role in your thinking, but a decision made apart from God is neither a wise decision nor a decision wisely made. If you need to know whether taking a stand is the right thing to do, first and foremost, ask God.

7. How do you usually make decisions about whether you should take some sort of stand—or respond to someone else's position— or let things go unaddressed?

8.   If you're rethinking your usual approach, what changes are you considering?

9.   What are the risks of taking a stand?

10. What are the risks of letting things go?

11. Why is it important to include God in your decision making about taking a stand?

READ MORE ABOUT IT

Read the story about the guards at the Tomb of the Unknowns in your *Stepping Up* book (page 29).

1.   Storms or not, why do these guards stay on duty?

2.   Does their example inspire you? If so, why?

3.   While many routine matters are under the control of the guards (condition of their uniforms and rifles, pace of their marching back and forth), other things are unpredictable (weather). In what ways does their faithful attention to the things they can control help them deal with the things they cannot?

TAKING INITIATIVE

GROUP DISCUSSION:
GATHERING AT BASE CAMP

1. What does it mean to take initiative?

2. In 1 Samuel 17:26, 32, David says of Goliath, "Who is this uncircumcised Philistine, that he should defy the armies of the living God? . . . Let no man's heart fail because of him. [I] will go and fight with this Philistine."

    How is it that David, who was just a boy, could fight the giant when all the older and more experienced soldiers were frozen by fear?

3. How is it that men like Bonhoeffer and the first responders of 9/11 were able to take initiative, when others were fleeing?

4. In today's culture, where do men struggle to take initiative?

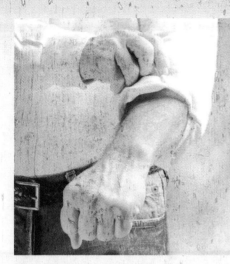

5. In your opinion, why does there seem to be a lack of initiative among young men today?

6. What are some ways to teach a young man how to take initiative?

From Your Time on the Trail (session 5)

7. What is one area where you need fresh resolve to "stand firm"? (See question 1, page 79.)

8. Why have you struggled to stand firm in this area? (See question 4, page 79.)

PERSONAL EXERCISE: LOGGING TIME ON THE TRAIL

DAY ONE

Some men take initiative in ways that don't show a great deal of wisdom. Like this guy.

Good intent, bad plan, and worse execution. This is not the kind of initiative we're recommending. Fortunately, other examples are more helpful. Consider the German army officers who tried to take down Hitler from within his own ranks—the true story that inspired the movie *Valkyrie*. These men saw the evil and danger behind the Nazi regime and set out to destroy it. Even though their plot failed, through the lens of history we see them as heroes because we admire their motive and bravery. While others looked away, they took action.

Initiate: to cause or facilitate the beginning of.

1. What does "taking initiative" mean to you?

2. What characterizes those who take initiative? What qualities about them do you most admire?

Men are meant to be initiators; they should set things in motion for the purpose of protecting, serving, and providing. Complacency has no rightful place in a man's life. He's meant to do things, to accomplish things. And for that he must *begin* things; he must initiate. While some men wait for life to happen, the men God uses happen to life. They are throttled up and ready for takeoff whenever He gives the order.

David is an excellent example. When he met up with his brothers in the Valley of Elah (see 1 Samuel 17), he found that they, along with the entire Israeli army, had retreated from battle and fled back to camp. It seems that a large man had been taunting them and scaring them . . . for forty days!

This was just too much for David. Despite his youth and inexperience in warfare, he saw what had to be done and took action. He didn't set out to be a hero or to make the other soldiers look bad. In fact, he wasn't thinking of himself at all. He clearly knew what God wanted and in faith he obeyed. A man of initiative if ever there was one.

3. What can you learn about taking initiative from David's encounter with Goliath?

4. What was different about David, in comparison with the members of the army, that made him the right man for this job?

5. In what ways was David prepared for this fight?

As much as we enjoy stories of heroism, we should also understand that taking initiative does not always mean being the first one to act. In some cases (think nonemergency), being the first to act or acting on instinct can do more harm than good. When it comes to taking initiative, wisdom often counts more than speed.

6. Perhaps you've heard someone say, "We need to do something even if it's wrong." What concerns you about that statement?

7. Can you think of a time when you saw someone act too quickly and in doing so made things worse instead of better? Describe what happened, and what should have been done instead.

By taking initiative we mean that men should lead lives of intentionality and purpose, rather than passivity and nonchalance. They should show concern for the life God has given them by pursuing His purpose and will, rather than wasting their days on self-indulgence. Starting now.

DAY TWO

> When David's time to die drew near, he commanded Solomon
> his son, saying, "I am about to go the way of all the earth. Be
> strong, and show yourself a man, and keep the charge of the
> LORD your God, walking in his ways and keeping his statutes,
> his commandments, his rules, and his testimonies, as it is
> written in the Law of Moses, that you may prosper in all that
> you do and wherever you turn." —1 KINGS 2:1–3

Last words. They sum up how we've tried to live and what we hope
our descendants will take forward through our legacy. David's words
to his son were all about walking with God. Nothing had mattered
more to him in life, and he hoped for nothing more—or less—for
his son.

1. If you knew you would be speaking your last words to your
family and close friends within the next few days, what would
you want to say?

2. The last words you just identified summarize what you want
your legacy to be. Is the general pattern of your life right now
helping to build that legacy? If not, what changes do you need
to make?

In his near-death words to his son, David challenged Solomon to take
the initiative to keep on track spiritually ("Be strong, and show
yourself a man, and keep the charge of the LORD your God, walking in
his ways . . ."). David recognized, as we all do, that there is a natural
tendency to drift from the ways of God.

3. What are some of the circumstances and events in life that draw us away from our devotion to God? (Check all that apply and add others that come to mind.)

- ☐ Physical fatigue
- ☐ Emotional overload
- ☐ Broken relationship
- ☐ Disappointment in a person you looked up to
- ☐ Personal moral failure
- ☐ Habitual sin you feel you can't overcome
- ☐ An inability to forgive someone who hurt you
- ☐ Death of a loved one
- ☐ Unjust things done to you during childhood and youth
- ☐ Significant life transition
- ☐ Unreasonable expectations others have of you
- ☐ Financial pressure
- ☐
- ☐
- ☐

Knowing that Solomon would face countless challenges in life—and knowing that no one could predict what exactly those challenges would be, how difficult they would be, and when they would come—David urged him to do the *one* thing that could prepare Solomon for anything: walk in the ways of God. David counseled him to live each day with clear spiritual focus.

4. What would Solomon need to do in order to maintain his spiritual focus?

Today we're concentrating on a man's need to take the initiative to develop and maintain his spiritual life. While we recognize there are other areas where initiative is also needed, we believe the spiritual life is foundational to the stability of every other area in a man's life.

+5. What steps do you need to take in order to develop and maintain your spiritual focus?

+6. Look back at the list given in question 3. Place a checkmark next to any of the items listed, including those you added to the list, that are issues of concern for you personally. In other words, what tends to erode your personal spiritual foundation?

DAY THREE

THE 360 REVIEW

An important part of manhood is learning to be teachable by seeking counsel from others. All men have blind spots; and though it's no fun to have them exposed, it's better for those you love—and for yourself in the long run—than continuing in ways that are hurtful and unhealthy.

One of the benefits we hope this study brings is to provide helpful ways for men to engage with one another about growing in godly manhood. Hopefully that is happening within your group. We also encourage you to reach out to others who can help you as well. That is why we're providing you with this 360 review.

The instructions are quite simple:

1. Make copies of the review on the facing page (or print it by going to MenSteppingUp.com).

2. Give the review to three to five people you trust and whose input you value, preferably one from each of the following categories: a friend, a close family member, a mentor, and your spouse. (Note: in this case we recommend that at least one of these should be female.)

3. Ask them to return your review within two weeks *because you will be working through this as part of an exercise in session 8.*

360 Review

As part of a study I am going through (Stepping Up), I need the input of several people who are close to me. Would you please take the time to complete this review and return it to me within the next ten days? Thanks so much for your time.

_____ (insert your name here)

1. Using a scale of 1–10, with 1 being low and 10 being high, rate me on the following. (If you have any comments, please write them on the back of this page.)

Standing Firm (being a man of integrity and conviction)

1: Wet noodle ⟶ 10: Washington Monument, without the cracks

Taking Initiative (setting the right things in motion for the right reasons)

1: Jellyfish ⟶ 10: Navy S.E.A.L.

Engaging with Wisdom and Grace (getting involved when I should and making situations better)

1: Remember the "bull in a ⟶ 10: You show the grace of a china shop"? Yeah, that's you. ballet dancer, and I don't even like ballet.

Planning Ahead and Providing (preparing myself and my loved ones for the future)

1: Mr. Las Vegas ⟶ 10: Mr. 401K

2. What five words would you use to describe me?

3. What one encouragement can you give me for something I do well?

4. What one caution can you give me for an improvement or adjustment I need to make?

+YOUR STEPPING UP PLAN

Continue developing your SUP by completing the following exercises.

1. Identify one area in your life where you need to do a better job of taking initiative. (Refer to the list given in the "A Step Beyond" section to prompt your thinking.) Write your answer in the Taking Initiative section on your SUP.

2. What's the first step you feel you need to take in order to take initiative in the area you just identified (refer to day 2, question 5)? Add this step to the Taking Initiative section on your SUP.

3. Whom could you talk to that could help? Perhaps one of the people who will be completing your 360 review? Write this person's name in the Taking Initiative section on your SUP.

4. What is your primary "Erosion Issue" when it comes to taking initiative, the issue that holds you back from doing what you feel God wants you to do (refer to day 2, question 6)? After giving this some thought, write your answer in the Taking Initiative section in your SUP.

A STEP BEYOND

In addition to his spiritual life, which we've already discussed, there are other areas in a man's life where he needs to take initiative to develop and care for properly:

Morality and integrity

Relationships, including

Marriage (or dating if single)

Children

Parents

Siblings

Friends

Colleagues

Employment or education

Personal finances

Physical condition

Living environment (house or apartment)

Civil responsibilities

1. What other areas should be added to the above list? Write them in the space provided above.

2. It is healthy to take time to occasionally evaluate how we are doing in the responsibilities and relationships God has given us. Take some time now, or set aside a specific time within the next few days, to work through the above list. In each area, ask,

Am I strong in this area or weak?

If weak, what could I do to grow stronger?

READ MORE ABOUT IT

On pages 105 and 106 in the book *Stepping Up*, Dennis Rainey described some of the excuses he has used to avoid taking initiative. Read that section and answer the following questions.

3. Do you identify with any of these excuses? If so, which do you identify with and why?

4. What other excuses have you used to avoid taking initiative?

5. What is God teaching you, either through this video series or through other sources, that will help you become more faithful in taking initiative?

TAKING THE INITIATIVE
TO SHARPEN YOUR MIND

One way to strengthen your resolve to take initiative is to read good books that educate and inspire. Mark Hamby, founder of Lamplighter Ministries, said a turning point in his Christian growth occurred when he was challenged by an older man to read more Christian biographies. He said, "Biographies were the catalysts God used in my life to inspire and instill a love for reading. I still quote from these literary treasures, and I still pray the prayers of these giants of the faith. I consider them my mentors and seek to follow their example. Much of who I am in Christ today I owe to these men and women whose lives challenged me to live passionately for Jesus Christ."[1]

He recommends the following biographies to get started. All eight are available through Lamplighter Ministries International at Lamplighter.net

Amy Carmichael – author and missionary to India for over 50 years in the late 1800s through early 1900s. She worked to rescue young girls from prostitution and established orphanages.

George Müller – famous for his work with orphans in England in the 1800s, Müller is believed to have cared for over 10,000 orphans and established over 100 schools. He was also famous for his life of faith, trusting God to provide for their needs and never asking for donations.

Gladys Aylward – worked among orphans in China in the mid 1900s. Helped to end the practice of binding the feet of young girls.

D. L. Moody – American evangelist in the late 1800s. Established Moody Bible Institute and inspired many to give their lives to missions all over the world.

Hudson Taylor – British missionary to China in the late 1800s. Founder of the China Inland Mission, which brought over 800 missionaries to the country and started 125 schools.

Behind Mr. Bunyan – a story from the perspective of a young lady who attended John Bunyan's church. Bunyan is most famously known for writing *Pilgrim's Progress* (see page 98).

If I Perish – story of the life of Ahn Ei Sook, a Japanese woman imprisoned and tortured for many years because of her refusal to bow to pagan idols.

Bruchko – account of the missionary adventures of Bruce Olson among the native tribes of South America.

R. Kent Hughes, author of *Disciplines of a Godly Man*, conducted a survey of a number of Christian leaders, asking what were the most influential books they had read. After the Bible, the following were some of the most often mentioned. (Note: Some works are more challenging than others. We've offered descriptions to help select a starting place.)

Mere Christianity by C. S. Lewis – written by the author of *The Chronicles of Narnia*, this book appeals to reason and paints a clear and concise picture of the essence of Christianity.

Institutes of the Christian Religion by John Calvin – an attempt by one of the early reformers to summarize the doctrines of this "new" faith. Calvin submitted a copy of his writing to the king of France in an effort to persuade him to adopt these beliefs and join the Reformation.

My Utmost for His Highest by Oswald Chambers – classic one-page-a-day devotional.

Brothers Karamazov by Fyodor Dostoyevski and *Anna Karenina* by Leo Tolstoy – two epic works of literature by Russian writers.

Shadow of the Almighty by Elisabeth Elliot – a summary of the life of her husband, Jim Elliot, and their work to reach the Huaorani (Auca) people in Ecuador.

Hudson Taylor's Spiritual Secret by Dr. and Mrs. Howard Taylor – biography of the famous missionary who worked in China during the 1800s.

The Pursuit of God by A. W. Tozer – timeless work on the importance of striving after God in all areas of life.

The Imitation of Christ by Thomas à Kempis – written by a German monk in the 1400s; thought to be the most widely read and translated Christian devotional work of all time.

Pilgrim's Progress by John Bunyan – an allegorical tale of a man named Christian and his journey toward the Celestial City; considered one of the most widely read English books of all time.

In His Steps by Charles Sheldon – written in the late 1800s, it is the story of a man who takes seriously the question "What Would Jesus Do?"

Loving God by Charles Colson – a figure from the Watergate scandal who later founded Prison Fellowship, Colson wrote this book on the importance of pursuing the first commandment and casting aside cultural Christianity.

Confessions by St. Augustine – autobiography of the early church's most influential theologian; focuses on his personal journey from rejecting Christ to embracing faith.

ENGAGING WITH
WISDOM AND GRACE

GROUP DISCUSSION: GATHERING AT BASE CAMP

1. Describe the worst boss you've had (hopefully he's not in the room right now).

2. Describe the best boss you've had.

3. What was the main difference between the two?

4. "Engaging with wisdom and grace" describes the concept of leadership from a Christ-centered perspective, loving others while also guiding them. What does it mean to be a servant who loves while at the same time being a leader who guides?

5. Why do we see so few true servant-leaders in the workplace and in our homes?

6. How can you do a better job of being a servant-leader?

From Your Time on the Trail (session 6)

7. What is an area where you need to show more initiative? (See question 1, page 94.)

8. What's the next step you need to take toward displaying initiative in this area? (See question 2, page 94.)

PERSONAL EXERCISE: LOGGING TIME ON THE TRAIL

DAY ONE

ENGAGING WITH WISDOM AND GRACE

Engaging with wisdom and grace is the ability to insert oneself into a situation to help improve it. This requires both the wisdom to know the proper timing and the grace to know how to tread. This is another way of describing leadership: helping others achieve more than is possible on their own.

We were reluctant to use the word *leadership* in this session because of how saturated our world is with this topic. There seems to be a self-proclaimed leadership guru on every other corner, and many people are so worn out with the idea that they'd rather just follow someone and forget about trying to lead. But it is precisely because of this excess that clear thinking is needed.

THE GOOD, THE BAD, AND THE LOUSY

Most people have had a boss, some good and some bad. Let's start with the bad. Think of some of the real loser bosses you've had.

1. What was it that made them such lousy bosses?

2. Now think of your better bosses. What did they do that made them great?

3. No doubt there are plenty of bad examples to draw from. Why do you think there is such a dearth of good leadership today?

4. When it comes to learning to lead, to engage with wisdom and grace, where do many people look for their examples and information today?

It is rather ironic that in an age when leadership is spoken about so much, there are still so many who do not do it well. The problem is not a lack of information, but a lack of understanding and applying some of the fundamental principles of engaging.

5. Think for a moment about the most essential components of engaging with wisdom and grace. What one or two qualities are required to engage well?

6. What keeps people from regularly practicing these qualities in their leadership?

Most people have some sense of what they want in a good boss, but they might struggle to apply these same ideas to their own leadership style when given an opportunity. Defining good leadership is no easy task, but you likely hit upon the essentials in the answers you've given in today's lesson. Good leadership, more than anything else, requires a proper biblical understanding of the idea, which we will explore more tomorrow.

> Sometimes if you suggest it, stepchildren object to it. A wise stepdad knows when to lead through his wife, that is, he utilizes her parental power to get things done when he can't. Stepkids may not realize how much he is leading and influencing the family from behind closed doors. As your relationship with the children deepens you can take a more "out in front" role.
>
> —RON L. DEAL

MOLOTOV THE FOLLOWER

The following is a joke that circulated through Communist Russia illustrating one type of leadership style:

There was a time in the 1940s when Vyacheslav Molotov was Soviet foreign minister. He was a shrewd man and a hard bargainer but worked for Josef Stalin. He was once overheard talking to Stalin by telephone during the course of some very intricate negotiations with the West. He said, "Yes, Comrade Stalin," in quiet tones, then again, "Yes, Comrade Stalin," and then, after a considerable wait, "Certainly, Comrade Stalin." Suddenly he was galvanized into emotion. "No, Comrade Stalin," he barked. "No. That's, no. Definitely, no. A thousand times, no!"

After a while, he quieted and it was "Yes, Comrade Stalin," again. The reporter who overheard this was probably never so excited in his life. Clearly, Molotov was daring to oppose the dictator on at least one point, and it would surely be important to the West to know what that point might be.

The reporter approached Molotov and said as calmly as possible, "Secretary Molotov, I could not help but hear you say at one point, 'No, Comrade Stalin.'"

Molotov turned his cold eyes on the reporter and said, "What of it?"

"May I ask," said the reporter, cautiously, "what the subject under discussion was at that time?"

"You may," said Molotov. "Comrade Stalin asked me if there was anything he had said with which I disagreed."[2]

DAY TWO

BIBLICAL LEADERSHIP

Biblical leadership is not a clear-cut topic. You can survey the Bible and come up with all kinds of conclusions about the issue. Take the great leaders from the Old Testament like Moses and David. They had their iconic successes, such as parting the Red Sea, overthrowing Pharaoh, uniting Israel, and slaying a giant. But they also had their challenges, such as watching God rain down plagues and poisonous serpents on their rebellious followers, or having a son try to overthrow his (David's) kingdom. Not the stuff that makes it into a book, *Moses, CEO.*

The point of many of these stories is not to show us how to lead a strategic initiative in the workplace. Rather, they all point toward the primary topic of the Bible: Jesus. Everything written somehow relates to the promise of God's redemption of the world in the person of Jesus Christ.

Thus you can't really talk about what the Bible has to say about leadership until you look at the life of Jesus. To be clear, this is no attempt to fully unpack the leadership "secrets" of Jesus. In fact, this approach will be laser focused on one simple passage from Jesus' teaching.

THE REQUEST: MARK 10

The Book of Mark is a book of action. In fact, in some Bible translations, most verses in Mark start with the word *and*. There is a constant motion, a continuous current of activity connected by one simple word that keeps things moving. This book certainly dives right into the action; within the first fifteen verses we're already launched into Jesus' preaching ministry, completely skipping the first twenty-nine years of His earthly life.

By the time we reach chapter 10, Jesus is gearing up for His entry into Jerusalem. These are His last moments outside the city before riding a donkey through the palm-laced Passover Day parade. But before He can go, two disciples approach Him to ask a very pressing question.

1. Read Mark 10:35–41. What did James and John ask?

2. How did Jesus respond?

3. How did the other disciples respond to James and John for asking what they did?

The answer was not likely what James and John hoped to hear, but even with the cryptic response, the rest of the disciples were still roused to resentment. Jesus, knowing their hearts, used this teachable moment to dig deeper and expose the root issue.

4. Read verses 42–45. How did Jesus describe the "rulers of the Gentiles"?

5. How did He compare this with the way the disciples should act?

What were the disciples seeking when they came to Jesus? Power, prestige, position; they wanted to be seen as important. They wanted to be in charge. Jesus exposed this desire by comparing them to the very people they despised: the rulers of the Gentiles (in their case, the Romans). Jesus exposed their hypocrisy: you don't want the Romans to rule, yet you want to be in charge! You want the same control for which you loathe the Romans.

But the reminder is potent—more so than they even knew—for Jesus then juxtaposed their desire with His example. In verse 45 He said, "For even the Son of Man came *not to be served* but *to serve,* and to give his life as a ransom for many" (emphasis added). You want to rule, but you need to sacrifice; you need to serve. Jesus would soon show them what it means to lead in a way they could not imagine. He was about to make the ultimate sacrifice on their behalf and give His life as a ransom, as a payment for their release.

In short, true leadership, according to this passage, is living out love for others. John 15:13 says, "Greater love has no one than this, that someone lays down his life for his friends." Leadership requires putting others before yourself, thinking of their needs before your own (Philippians 2:3), which is how every person who ever lived wants to be treated by others. This principle becomes hard to apply, however, when you are in the position of power.

Biblical leadership is love.

Engaging with wisdom and grace requires love. It requires that we think of the needs of others as more important than our own. No easy task. For that we must depend upon the guidance of the Holy Spirit.

DAY THREE

EVALUATING YOUR ENGAGEMENT

History is replete with leaders of all types. There are the conquering military types like Napoleon, Alexander the Great, and Robert E. Lee. The force of their personalities, combined with their military brilliance, inspired nations to follow along for the conquest. Then there are the orators, the great motivational leaders like Winston Churchill, Ronald Reagan, and William Wallace—men who stirred throngs with their words and ideas. There are also the unconventional leaders, those who take the indirect paths, such as Martin Luther King Jr., Gandhi, and Joan of Arc, who launched revolutions from the bottom up, creating momentum through leading by example and living out their convictions.

1. What characteristics in a leader are most important to you?

2. How do you hope other people would describe your leadership style?

3. What word would you use to describe the way you lead people?

One of the hardest things in life is to see your own blind spots, to be objectively aware of your flaws. And, honestly, who really wants to focus on these failures? It's certainly no fun to dwell on the details of your shortcomings. And no doubt leadership is one of the hardest areas to analyze objectively.

Maybe you've been too domineering. Or maybe you've been too passive, failing to engage at all when your leadership was desperately needed.

+4. Is there an area of your life where you have struggled to properly engage with wisdom and grace in the way you lead others? (If you are having trouble thinking of something, this may be a blind spot.)

+5. Why do you think you've struggled in this area? What is the underlying issue that erodes your ability to engage with wisdom and grace?

+6. List one or two action steps you can take this week to begin engaging with wisdom and grace in the area you identified in question 4.

+7. Encouragement is such an important part of following through. Whom could you talk to that could help motivate and train you to develop a biblical style of leadership?

+YOUR STEPPING UP PLAN

Add the following information to your SUP.

1. Identify one area in your life where you feel you need to do a better job in leadership by learning to engage with wisdom and grace. Your answer to day 3, question 4 may help. Write your answer in the Engaging with Wisdom and Grace section on your SUP.

2. What step do you need to take (refer to day 3, question 6)? Add this step to the Engaging with Wisdom and Grace section on your SUP.

3. Whom could you talk to that could help you grow in this area of leadership (see day 3, question 7)? Write this person's name in the Engaging with Wisdom and Grace section on your SUP.

4. What is your primary "Erosion Issue" when it comes to leading with wisdom and grace, the issue that seems to give you the most trouble in this area (refer to day 3, question 5)? After giving this some thought, write your answer in the Engaging with Wisdom and Grace section on your SUP.

A STEP BEYOND

BROKEN ENGAGEMENT

Engaging with wisdom and grace is part of being a man. From the beginning of the Bible, God placed men in a position to trust Him in order to accomplish great things. Yet anyone who has tried to engage knows there are countless challenges to overcome. If God Himself had His first two direct reports go AWOL, then you'd be delusional not to expect that some things will go wrong for you.

1. What are some of the main challenges men face in engaging with wisdom and grace?

2. There seems to be heaps of hesitancy among men today, almost like they are scared to lead. What advice would you give to a guy who is too timid to take the lead?

3. What verses of scripture would you direct him to?

Some men are just risk averse, afraid to rock the boat because they might get wet. For some it's a performance issue, fear of failure, of the unknown, or the unpredictable. And others are just plain ol' apathetic.

4. Think back to a time when you failed to lead, when you stumbled out of the starting gate. What were the underlying reasons that blocked your leadership? (Consider both the internal and external circumstances that were at play.)

Identifying these reasons can be a huge help in overcoming the reluctance to lead. Many men never come to understand the root issue behind their staggering and failures. It is important to dig below the surface.

Think back to yesterday's lesson and the area you identified where you need to do a better job of engaging. As you think about that area, what is the underlying issue that has kept you from leading like you desire? As you process this, make sure to not only think about the actual circumstance, but also try to dig deeper to the reason behind the circumstance. For instance, "My wife didn't like my decision" would be the circumstance, but the root issue might be "I'm a people pleaser," or "I struggle with self-esteem and want people to like me," or "I often dismiss other people's ideas and struggle with pride."

5.   What root issue did you identify?

6.   What do you need to do to address the root issue in your life?

READ MORE ABOUT IT

In the *Stepping Up* book, read the story of Winston Churchill in the first part of chapter 9, pages 67–70.

Part of engaging with wisdom and grace is staying engaged even when the battle appears to be lost and everyone is against you. Churchill had a firm conviction that the English people were threatened by Hitler, and he stuck by this conviction, even when it meant political death.

7.   Is there an area of your life where you need this kind of courage to stay engaged? It could be a social issue or a personal one. Maybe something you are personally passionate about or an apparent danger lurking on the horizon for someone you love.

SOLON AND THE ATHENIAN DILEMMA

History has experienced a wide array of leaders, many of which seemed to lean more toward dictator than democrat. Ancient Greece is often seen as an exception to the rule, heralded as the place where modern man has his roots, where the firstfruits of democracy are realized.

Athens, one of the prominent cities of ancient Greece and the cradle of modern civilization, must be placed in this pantheon of politics by properly understanding its history. Now celebrated, there was a season when the Athenian government had lost its way, had turned the common man into a slave, and was on the verge of the collapse of society as they knew it.

Drastic times called for drastic measures. And drastic they were! The Athenians realized they desperately needed a new set of laws, so they called upon one man to rewrite the laws. The man in their favor was their national poet, their sage, the Grecian version of Confucius. That man's name was Solon; and rewrite the laws he did!

Now just try to imagine this: America, on the verge of financial and social collapse, decides to bring in Robert Frost or Ernest Hemingway to rewrite the laws. Everything rests on the shoulders of one man. Every citizen waits for the new laws as the constitution is ripped apart and repurposed as toilet paper. Jefferson and Madison are rolling in their graves.

But the Athenians submitted to Solon's serenade, as he said so long and farewell to the old ways. He "immediately canceled all debts, forbade the practice of enslaving for debt, free[d] those already enslaved for debt, and re-purchased those sold abroad."[1] He also established a court and legal system and gave the average citizen the right to bring an issue to the courts. Probably his most important reform was to encourage olive harvesting and pottery production. This turned their economy around and pushed them to trade with other countries.

Most men, if given a chance, would likely rewrite the laws for their own benefit (like demanding box seats at ball games and establishing free cheesecake Fridays). But Solon focused on the needs of the common man and revived the nation. And he did it with a

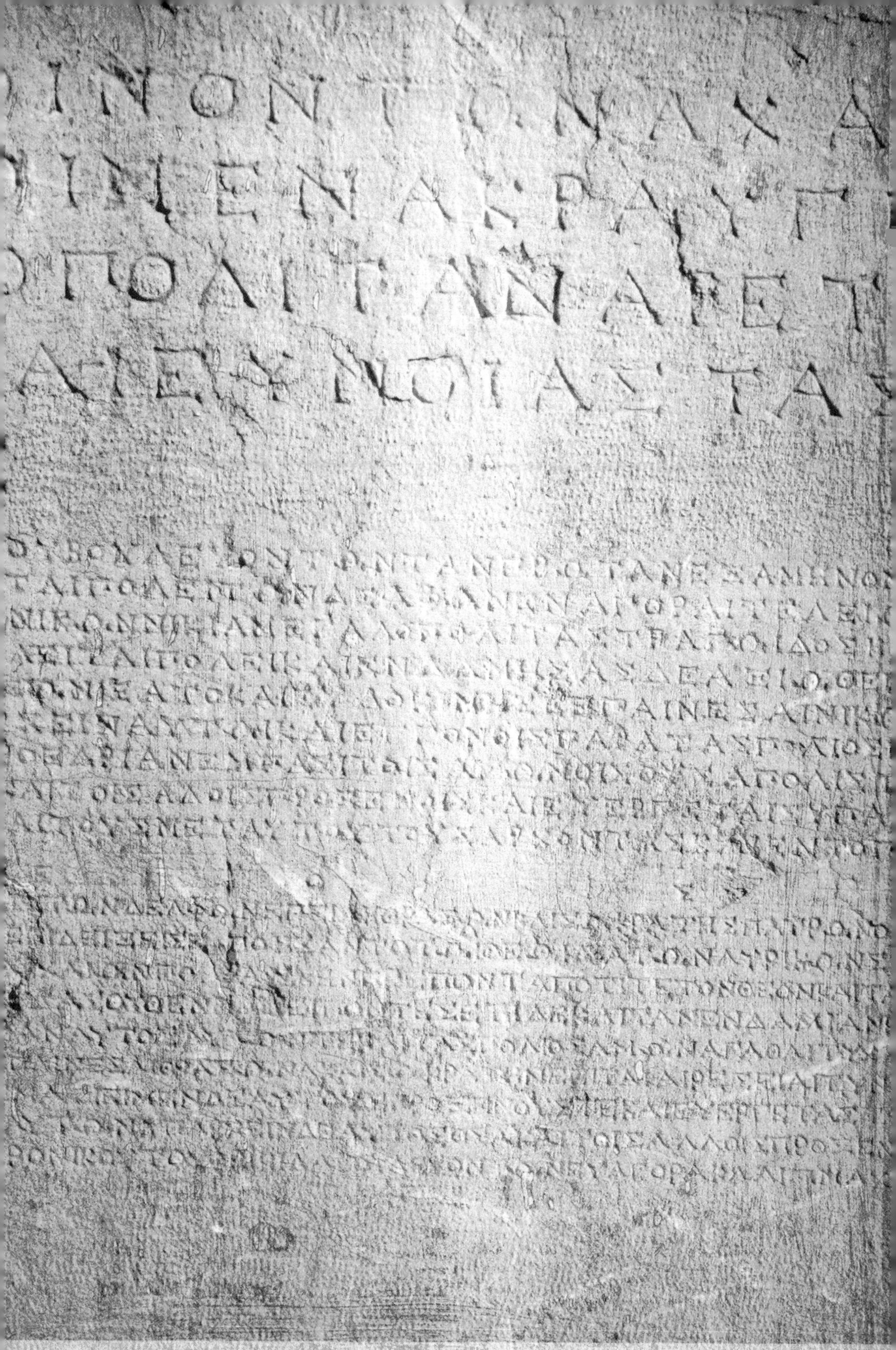

style of leadership that had been ignored up to that point—he practiced the basic idea of "love your neighbor as yourself."

Solon's last act of leadership was to leave town for ten years, knowing his laws could be established only if he were out of the picture. He truly set aside his own ego for the good of the nation. This is leadership at its finest—thinking of others first, or, as Paul said, "Let each of you look not only to his own interests, but also to the interests of others" (Philippians 2:4).

PLANNING AND PROVIDING

GROUP DISCUSSION:
GATHERING AT BASE CAMP

1. We're told that a man should provide for his family. What have you understood this to mean?

2. What new ways of defining the role of man as a provider came out in the video?

   The video adds the idea of "seeing ahead" to the traditional definition of providing. This means to see both opportunities and problems in advance and to begin to prepare for them. In what ways does this broaden your understanding of your role as a man?

3. What opportunities and problems do you see coming toward you and your family in the next few years?

4. What can you begin doing now to prepare for these opportunities and problems?

5. If you were writing a personal mission statement, a sentence or two that would state your purpose in life, what might you include in it?

6. Proverbs 16:9 says, "The heart of man plans his way, but the LORD establishes his steps." How does one trust the sovereignty of God when plans go awry? (You might share a specific example of how you wrestled with this during a challenging circumstance in your life).

From Your Time on the Trail (session 7)

7. Name an area you identified where you need to practice "engaging with wisdom and grace." How do you hope to handle this area differently in the future? (See question 4, page 110.)

8. How do you hope to apply Jesus' example of leadership in your life? (Refer to session 7, day 2.)

PERSONAL EXERCISE: LOGGING TIME ON THE TRAIL

DAY ONE

THE SCOUT

Reflecting on one of his favorite television programs from boyhood, *Wagon Train,* author Stu Weber described what it means for a man to be a provider.

> Those [the scout's] were the cowboy boots I wanted to crawl into. That was the job I wanted. It was Flint McCullough who always rode miles out in front of that long, ponderous caravan. Flint McCullough, the ever-vigilant eyes and ears of the wagon train. Flint McCullough, probing out ahead, checking out the trail, looking for Indians, scouting out water holes, scanning the shimmering skyline with young eyes made old and wise by the miles he had ridden and the things he had seen. He was the first to smell danger, dodge the arrows, hear the muted thunder of faraway buffalo herds, and taste the bite of distant blizzards riding on the prairie wind. It was up to him to spot potential hazards, discern lurking enemies, and pick out the best and safest trail for the train to follow. . . .
>
> . . . That whole rolling community of men, women, and children relied on McCullough's experience, alert judgment, and unfailing sense of direction. It was a dangerous thing, after all, this business of uprooting from comfortable homes and picket-fenced yards, putting your worldly goods and precious family into a wagon and setting off across a vast, trackless continent. The immigrants in their wagons couldn't see all the dangers ahead. They couldn't imagine what threatened over the next rise. They didn't know where to find water for their barrels or grass for their livestock.
>
> They had to rely on The Scout.
>
> It's always the image of Flint McCullough that swims into my mind as I think about the role of a man as a provider for his family. Now, that wouldn't make much sense if you thought

only of the traditional definition of "provider." In our culture, when we think of provision, we think of food on the table and a roof over our heads. Actually, the emphasis on provision is *vision*. The *pro* part of the word indicates "before" or "ahead of time." *Vision* obviously speaks of "sight" or "seeing." What does that formula yield?

Looking ahead. Giving direction. Anticipating needs. Defining destination. Riding ahead of the wagon on scout duty.[1]

1. How does Weber's description help you better understand the role of a provider?

2. What types of things is a man responsible to "scout" for in his own life?

3. If he's married, what types of things should a man scout for on behalf of his wife?

4. If he's a dad, what types of things should a man scout for on behalf of his children?

The men who are the best providers are those who live intentionally (there's that word again). They are alert, watchful, and cautious, though not fearful. They know where they are strong and where they are vulnerable. If they are married and if they have children, they also know the strengths and vulnerabilities of their family members. They are proactive in their pursuit of God, knowing that apart from Him they can do nothing (John 15:5). They have a general sense of direction for their life and for those under their care. They look to the future with faith and hope.

5. If this describes any of the men you know, write their names here.

Note: You'll be evaluating your 360 reviews (from session 6) in two days. Make sure to get these back as soon as possible.

DAY TWO

> He chose David his servant and took him from the sheepfolds;
> from following the nursing ewes he brought him to shepherd
> Jacob his people, Israel his inheritance. With upright heart
> he [David] shepherded them and guided them with his
> skillful hand. —PSALM 78:70–72

Yesterday we looked at the role of a provider, one who looks ahead, anticipates needs, gives direction, and prepares for the future. Given that description, who is a better provider than God Himself? There are many ways that God provides for us beyond placing a roof over our heads, clothes on our backs, and food at our tables—the kinds of things we typically think a provider does. But throughout our lives, if we are of a mind to acknowledge the work of God, we will see countless ways He has been providing.

Sometimes God provides by preparing us for events or circumstances that, though we can't foresee them, He knows we will encounter later in life. For example, He may have us endure a time of illness because He knows we will later need compassion and patience to care for others. He may teach us principles of endurance, exercise, and self-control as young men so we will be prepared to apply those lessons to other areas of life later on. He may give us a bad boss to teach us how to be a good one. God provides for us by preparing us.

1. Reflect on your life to see if you can come up with any examples of ways God prepared you for circumstances you couldn't foresee. List a few of those examples here.

Another way that God provides is by bringing people into our lives who help to shape us.

According to Psalm 78 (see above), God knew His people needed a certain kind of leader, someone who was brave, wise, and had a heart of integrity. They needed someone who wouldn't compromise on God's standards or question His directives. Someone who bore the scars of battle but not the arrogance of victory. A faithful and dependable man. So God provided them with David.

2. Who has God brought into your life to help shape you? Take some time to list the names of your "key influencers" below. The list might include people who have been in your life for many years, or even some whom you knew only briefly but left a big impression.

3. Now, go back through your list and write a brief description that summarizes how God used each person to influence you.

4. Finally, would you take a few minutes to pray and thank God for each person on your list?

David's upbringing as a shepherd had prepared him for the new assignment God gave him: being king. He had grown up in a hard-working and sometimes dangerous environment. Day after day and night after night, David had been the protector of the flock. He regularly put his comfort and safety aside to keep the sheep from harm. (If you were to compare Psalm 23, which describes the work a shepherd does to care for his flock, with the description of "The Scout" in yesterday's exercise, you'd see many similarities.)

The sovereignty of God should not make you passive, but give you the courage to engage with Him at every turn and in every decision.

David, the one God provided, also became a provider himself. This is true of every man. God prepares and shapes him so that He (God) can use that man to provide and care for others. Whether married or single, a father or not, a man has a God-given duty to provide. To be a scout. To be a shepherd. To put the needs and care of others ahead of his own.

5. Who are the people God has given you to care for, to provide for? List them here, and remember that this doesn't just refer to immediate family members; your list could include people you are influencing in your extended family, at work, in your church, or in your community.

Psalm 78:72 specifies two things that characterized David's leadership: an upright heart and skill. These are not the only qualities a man needs in order to live and lead well, but they are at the top of the list. Are these being developed in your life?

6. What does it mean to have an "upright heart"?

7. What are some of the skills God has built into your life, and how are you using these skills to serve and provide for others?

READ MORE ABOUT IT

Read chapter 20, "Becoming a Generational Messenger" in your *Stepping Up* book (pages 153–161).

DAY THREE

What are you doing to prepare yourself to be a good provider or to become a better one? (Again, we're not just talking about the usual sense of being a provider.) Are you actively pursuing a life of godliness that includes such qualities as honor, integrity, diligence, humility, and wisdom? These are all things we like to talk about and admire in others, but the question is . . . do they characterize you?

Most likely you are interested in being this kind of man or you wouldn't be doing this study. And you certainly wouldn't have made it to session 8! So we'll go with the assumption that godly character is your goal.

THE 360 REVIEW

Back in session 6 we encouraged you to solicit the input of some friends through a 360 review. Let's now unpack some of the information you collected through that exercise.

1. Taking into account all the reviews you got back, where do you seem to be strongest?

2. Where do you seem to be most in need of growth and development?

3. Did any of the feedback from the 360 review surprise you? Explain what surprised you and why.

NOW AND THEN

How many times have you heard someone remark about how quickly time seems to be moving? These comments are often made with a tinge of regret, as if the speaker would do things differently if given the chance. Certainly we all have regrets, some bigger than others, but there is a way to minimize them and to soften their blow, and that is to become a better provider, a better scout.

While the Bible tells us not to worry about tomorrow (Matthew 6:34), that doesn't mean we shouldn't give any thought to what lies ahead. In fact, Jesus had plenty to say about the wisdom of living in light of future events, the most significant of which will be His return (Matthew 24:36–44). We're not to be worrying, but we are to be preparing.

It is because of this most important and certain future event that we should be men who prepare and provide in ways that will not shame us when we meet our Lord. Every man has a high and holy calling on his life. He should live each day within a context that not only includes God, but makes Him supreme. You will be a better man, a better husband, a better dad, a better friend, a better everything if God is your foremost loyalty.

+4. Is God your foremost loyalty? If not, what other relationships or pursuits tend to rival Him in your life?

+5. As you've been thinking about being a provider, in what two or three areas in your life do you need to improve?

+6. What steps do you need to take to become a better provider?

+7. We are often helped by talking with others. Yesterday you were asked to list some of the key influencers in your life. Perhaps you want to consult with one of them, or another person, to seek their help in developing this area of your life. Who is that person you would like to talk to?

DAY FOUR

YOUR MISSION STATEMENT

FIRST PASS

The 360 review (that we looked at yesterday) isn't really complete until you answer some questions about yourself. But we're going to ask you a different set of questions, hoping that your responses will help you draft a personal mission statement. (Some of you just salivated and some of you groaned, but we think even the groaners will find this exercise relatively painless and greatly helpful.) So, let's get started.

1. What are you particularly skilled at doing?

2. What could you lose all track of time while doing? (Think productive work, not playtime.)

3. What are you doing when you're most courageous and confident?

4. What causes or needs move you emotionally and stir you to want to take action?

5. Who are your heroes, and what makes them heroic to you?

6. What would you love to give your life to, and why?

7. What are your biggest life lessons, things you learned through personal experience, that have had a lasting impact on you?

8. If you could ask God to let you accomplish one thing with your life, what would that one thing be?

SECOND PASS

That's a lot of heart-searching, isn't it? But it's also quite revealing. The answers to questions like these show how God has been working to shape your life and give strong indications of the ways He wants to use you to influence the world.

Let's take another step toward drafting your personal mission statement by taking your answers from your First Pass and completing the following statements.

9. God has given me the skill to _____.

10. I most feel the approval of God when I'm _____
_____.

11. I am greatly moved to take action when I see/hear about people who need _____.

12. I would love to be able to _____
_____.

FINAL PRODUCT

Finally, take the responses you wrote in the blanks above and form them into one two-part statement.

13. Because God (describe what He has built into your life through skills and personal experience) _____
_____
_____ ,

I believe He wants to use me to _____
_____.

+YOUR STEPPING UP PLAN

Continue developing your SUP by adding the following information to it.

1. Identify one area in your life where you need to become a better provider (your answer to day 3, question 5 may help). Write your answer in the Planning and Providing section on your SUP.

2. What step do you need to take toward improving in this area of your life (refer to day 3, question 6)? Add this step to your SUP.

3. Who could you talk to that could help you become a better provider and planner (refer to day 3, question 7)? Write this person's name in the Planning and Providing section on your SUP.

4. What is your primary "Erosion Issue" in this area, the issue that holds you back the most when it comes to planning ahead and providing? (Your answer to day 3, question 4 might prompt your thinking.) Add your answer to your SUP.

5. Today you worked on developing a personal mission statement. Transfer your statement to your SUP.

HAVING A
VISION

FOR YOUR MARRIAGE AND FAMILY

GROUP DISCUSSION:
GATHERING AT BASE CAMP

1. The "Buy Your Children" video segment was intentionally absurd. Who would even suggest such a thing in real life? But it illustrates how men have sacrificed their family for things that seem important. What things do men allow to take a higher priority than their family?

2. What things tend to compete with the priority of family in *your* life?

3. Do you find it difficult to pray regularly with your wife? If so, why?

4. Dan Allender told about a time when he encouraged his wife to grow in her area of gifting. Explain why this is a good thing for a husband to do.

5. What would you say to your wife, what interest or gifting should she pursue?

6. Who are some men that have done a good job of intentionally meeting the needs in their family? What specifically did they do well?

From Your Time on the Trail (session 8)

7. How do you need to do a better job of providing? (Keep in mind that we're referring to the concept of "pro-vision" rather than merely the financial aspect of providing)(See question 5, page 127.)

8. What did you learn from the 360 review that you're willing to share? (Take a risk and share from both the encouragement and the criticism you received.)

PERSONAL EXERCISE: LOGGING TIME ON THE TRAIL

DAY ONE

Note: This session is heavily focused on marriage and family. If you are not married or do not have children, try to think in terms of the legacy you want to leave in the lives of others. Consider your most important relationships: a sibling, friend, extended family member, or the children God may give you in the future.

THE VISION

What does it mean for a man to have a vision for his marriage and his family? Thinking back to session 8 and the concept of "pro-vision," or "seeing ahead," it starts with the "seeing" part, having a picture in your mind of where you want things to be. It may start small, with just a glimmer of an idea. Some men will eventually take this image and really flesh it out, paint the full portrait across a large canvas, while others will just have a few doodles in their sketchbook. No matter where you are in the process, this session is about helping you clarify a vision for marriage and family.

But let's start by answering the big question: Why? Why is this important?

1. Why is it important to set a vision and direction for your family?

> The heart of man plans his way, but the Lord establishes his steps.
>
> **—PROVERBS 16:9**

PRODUCTIVE PAIN

Some guys get really excited about this kind of thing, while others would rather have dental work done. But dental work doesn't have to be painful, and neither does casting a vision for your family.

There are no narcotics included with this study, but understanding the "why" may help numb the pain. Here are reasons to set a vision and direction for your family.

1. From the beginning of the Bible, God calls men to lead. He calls them to set a direction and guide their families, especially in their efforts to connect with God.

2. God Himself models this by the way He established creation, created order out of chaos, and gave vision and direction to the people He placed on earth.

3. The Old Testament contains numerous bad examples of fathers not leading and the problems that occur as a result (David with Absalom in 2 Samuel 13–18, Eli and his sons in 1 Samuel 2–4).

4. If you don't set a direction for your family, who will? You can hope that your family will head the right direction, but how can you be sure they know where to go? Every ship needs a captain setting the course and plotting the voyage. Otherwise the crew is left to float aimlessly, drifting with whatever wind or current passes through the course of life. If *you* don't set the course, then you'll be counting on chance, hoping the best breeze blows through at the right moment.

5. Finally, as a man, you have a lot to offer. You have ideas, character, and values that were passed on to you from your family and mentors. You have been given a great privilege and responsibility to continue that heritage by passing it on to others.

VALUES

2. When you think of the values that were passed on to you, and that you would want to pass on to others, what comes to mind? Check all of the following that apply and list any others.

☐ Character

☐ Integrity

☐ Strong work ethic

☐ Sense of humor

☐ Spontaneity

☐ Love for God

☐ Desire to share your faith

☐ Determination

☐ Respect for authority

☐ Entrepreneurial spirit

☐ Servant attitude

☐ Commitment to quality

☐ Concern for the poor

☐ Self-starter

☐ Commitment to missions and giving

☐ Love for others

☐ Love for the Bible

☐ Other:

3. Now, try to reduce the above list to the top five values you want to pass on.

1.

2.

3.

4.

5.

4. There is no perfect set of values for a family and no perfect way to make them a priority, but identifying what's important to you is a great start. If you are married, take some time this week to talk with your wife about these values and capture her thoughts below.

DAY TWO

ARROWS IN THE HAND

> Like arrows in the hand of a warrior are the children of one's youth. Blessed is the man who fills his quiver with them! He shall not be put to shame when he speaks with his enemies in the gate. —PSALM 127:4–5

These verses emphasize the importance of children, of having them and launching them well. Of course, not everyone has children, so you'll need to apply what we're about to unpack to your own experience, but stay with us on this. If your children are long gone, think of ways you can invest in parents of young children. If you are a young single guy, there is no better time to start thinking about this. If you can think now about how you want to approach your children, it will change the way you plan your career, your dreams, the way you date and approach marriage.

1. The metaphor used for children in this section is arrows. How does it change your view of children to think of them like an arrow?

2. Drawing a bow and aiming an arrow well requires skill, strength, patience, and practice. In fact, much of the destiny of the arrow depends upon the way the warrior handles the arrow. How does it shape your perspective on raising children to think of a parent as a warrior?

To aim an arrow well you need to have a good idea of the target, where you intend to fire the arrow. This is the "vision" part of these verses. An arrow is most effective when the target is clear in the mind of the warrior. A parent must learn to define the target.

3. This might be difficult, but think in terms of the overall goal for a child. Where should he end up? What should his future look like? Describe this in a sentence or two. (Think in terms of your child's moral, spiritual, physical, and emotional health.)

We've talked about the importance of knowing how to use an arrow, how to aim it well, and having a clear idea of the target. There's also a big emphasis in these verses on the importance of simply *having* arrows. When one's quiver is full, he's a blessed man.

4. How does this view of children compare to the way children are often viewed?

5. What does the last part of verse 5 say are the benefits of having a quiver full of children?

The emphasis here is on protection, on seeing children as a security against one's enemies, against an uncertain future. Children are the means by which your life and legacy continue. Children are, as Neil Postman said, "the living messages we send to a time we will not see."[1]

STRENGTH BEHIND THE BOW

As stated earlier, aiming an arrow requires skill and focus. You can choose the target on your own, but a key aspect of aiming an arrow well is understanding the true strength behind the warrior.

> Unless the LORD builds the house, those who build it labor in vain. Unless the LORD watches over the city, the watchman stays awake in vain. —PSALM 127:1–2

6. What do the first two verses of Psalm 127 have to say about the ultimate source of our protection?

These verses set things in their proper order. Yes, arrows are important, but ultimately, it is the Lord who watches and builds. Putting trust in the wrong thing will leave one unbalanced and vulnerable to attack.

The truly comforting part of this reality is the added trust in the sovereignty of God. If the destiny of an arrow rested fully on the warrior, it would be rather daunting. Many parents have wondered how much they were screwing up their child at any given moment. But knowing that the Lord builds the house adds relief; you can trust Him to give guidance to the arrow as well. Yes, plan and set direction and vision, but also know that God is ultimately the one who works in the heart of a child to direct him properly.

> I planted, Apollos watered, but God gave the growth.
>
> —1 CORINTHIANS 3:6

DAY THREE

SETTING VISION

Think back to the video segment where Dan Allender talked about the meeting he had with his wife. During that time he identified and edified her strengths, encouraging her to take steps to develop those gifts. No doubt this was a powerful moment for her and for their marriage, a moment when Dan took the initiative to lead his wife and cast a vision for her. This is the kind of thing we want to help you think about today. This story is a great example of a tangible step you can take in casting vision for your wife and/or family.

1. How would you rate yourself in setting a vision for your family? (This question isn't meant to get you down, but just to take stock of where you are.) Rate yourself on the following scale:

    1   2   3   4   5   6   7   8   9   10
    | |
    I can't even   The United
    spell *vision*   Nations could
                                        learn a few things
                                        from me about
                                        setting direction.

+2. What are some challenges you've faced in casting vision for your marriage and family in the past? What has undermined your ability to be successful with this? Check all that apply, then circle the one that has caused you the most trouble.

    ☐ Fear that others won't listen to me or follow my lead

    ☐ Lack of motivation

    ☐ Plain ol' passivity

    ☐ Too busy with other things

    ☐ Afraid of coming across as too controlling or dictatorial

    ☐ Wasn't even aware that I should do this

    ☐ Shame from past failures in relationships

    ☐ Other:

ONE AREA

It's not necessary to develop an elaborate master plan for every month of the next ten years to cast a vision for your family. Having one simple step to take can make a huge difference. Thus our aim is to help you keep things as simple as possible (though simple is not always easy). You may already have an area in mind that you need to address, but let's start by just thinking of a person who needs you to set a vision right now. (List a name in each category below.)

3. Circle the name of that one person who most needs vision direction right now.

Wife: _____ (name)

Child: _____ (name)

Sibling: _____ (name)

Friend: _____ (name)

+4. Why did that person come to mind? Is there one particular issue in the individual's life that needs to be addressed? If so, describe that issue.

+5. What are some things you could say to that person to help cast vision for them? (Some of the following categories might help.) Keep in mind that you are not casting judgment on this person, but rather are thinking of ways you can help him be all God created him to be.

Areas where he needs encouragement

Specific things you appreciate about her

Something he does well that he could develop

An area of weakness that is holding her back

I could say:

+6. What is the next step you need to take toward having this conversation? (Also consider: Is there anyone else you need to connect with before meeting with this person? Anyone who could give you feedback or ideas?)

FOR SINGLE GUYS

+7. Take a moment and think about how you are becoming the kind of future husband you need to be. Is there one area you need to take care of now to best prepare yourself for leading a family? Look at the following list and try to identify one area.

☐ Get out of debt

☐ Establish my career

☐ Grow in my understanding of the Bible

☐ Deal with lust issues in my life

☐ Learn to treat women honorably

☐ Learn to serve others well

☐ Other:

+YOUR STEPPING UP PLAN

Add the following information to your SUP.

1. Identify one area where you need to clarify and communicate your vision for your family (your answers to day 3, questions 4 and 5 may help). If you are a single man, what should you be doing to prepare for leading a family (refer to you answer to day 3, question 7)? Write your answer in the Family Vision section on your SUP.

2. What step do you need to take toward improving in this area of your life (refer to day 3, question 6)? Add this step to your SUP.

3. Who could you talk to that could help (refer to day 3, question 6)? Write this person's name in the Family Vision section on your SUP.

4. What is your primary "Erosion Issue" here, the issue that undermines your consistency in leading your family with clear vision? (Your answer to day 3, question 2 might prompt your thinking.) Add your answer to your SUP.

Supplemental Readings and Exercises for Session 9

CHALLENGES FOR LEADING YOUR FAMILY

Probably one of the greatest challenges you'll face in casting vision for your marriage and family is finding the time and energy to engage the issue. Here are a couple of tools that should help make things a bit easier for you.

Ten Questions

Pastor Tom Elliff developed a list of ten questions you can use to begin the conversation with your wife:[2]

1. What could I do to make you feel more loved?

2. What could I do to make you feel more respected?

3. What could I do to make you feel more understood?

4. What could I do to make you more secure?

5. What could I do to make you feel more confident in our future direction?

6. What attribute would you like me to develop?

7. What attribute would you like me to help you develop?

8. What achievement in my life would bring you the greatest joy?

9. What would indicate to you that I really desire to be more Christlike?

10. What mutual goal would you like to see us accomplish?

You can find the list in chapter 14 of *Stepping Up* (page 106) along with more explanation of how Tom and his wife have used these questions to strengthen their marriage.

Getting Away to Get It Together

This is a short book (by Bill and Carolyn Wellons) that equips you and your spouse for a weekend discussion about your family's vision and goals. It includes a series of exercises and questions to guide you through the weekend, along with ideas for preparing for the getaway (available through ShopFamilyLife.com).

Visionary Family Ministries

For additional help, make sure to check out Rob Rienow's ministry (Rob was featured in this week's video session) called Visionary Family Ministries (VisionaryFam.com). They offer conferences and resources to help you set a clear vision and direction for your family.

READ MORE ABOUT IT

Read the story of Jackie Robinson on pages 137–142 in the *Stepping Up* book.

    1. What was Branch Rickey's vision for Robinson?

    2. Why do you think Robinson was willing to endure the endless insults and prejudice that he did?

    3. What vision do you think Robinson had for his own family?

Read pages 142–144, "20/20 Generational Vision," in the *Stepping Up* book.

    1. How does providing vision and leadership require men "to look past themselves"?

    2. How would you define "20/20 generational vision"?

THE GETAWAY PLAN

When was the last time you got away with your spouse to talk, play, and plan together?

BY ROB FLOOD[8]

The Need for Getting Away

In his book *Disciplines of a Godly Man*, R. Kent Hughes tells this story:

> Years ago, in the Midwest, a farmer and his wife were lying in bed during a storm when the funnel of a tornado suddenly lifted the roof right off the house and sucked their bed away with them still in it. The wife began to cry, and the farmer called to her that it was no time to cry. She called back that she was so happy, she could not help it—it was the first time they had been out together in twenty years!

One of the greatest needs of any married couple is for unhurried time together. And it's amazing how many couples go years without ever getting away for a day or weekend together.

If we cannot make room in our schedules for solid communication with our spouses, then we are just too busy. How can we understand each other if we never take the time to really hear each other? The truth is . . . we can't.

As busy as we are, we need to go out and claim that alone time. We must make it a priority.

Our Model for Getting Away

Whenever we try to explain away or justify our busyness, we should consider the example provided by Jesus. A good example is found in Mark 6. After the miraculous meal of feeding the multitudes, Jesus sent His disciples across the sea while He remained. "And after he had taken leave of them, he went up on the mountain to pray" (Mark 6:46). This was late in the evening. At other times, He got away from the noise early in the morning. (See Matthew 14 and Mark 1.)

Surely, the importance of our daily tasks pales in comparison to the importance of Christ's work when He walked the earth. Yet, through all of the demands on His time, He regularly got away to be alone. The lesson is clear: Sometimes busyness must yield to the importance of necessary communication. This is true of your relationship with God; it is also true of your relationship with your spouse.

Encouragement for Getting Away

One couple believes the greatest benefit of getting away regularly for a weekend together has been their joint decisions on family priorities. The husband said, "All the little arguments about priorities are avoided because we decide our priorities over the weekend. Now, when something comes up and we have to make a decision on it, we revisit our goals from the weekend and see if it fits within those goals. If not, we feel complete freedom to say no."

His wife says, "Another big benefit to our relationship is just that I feel loved when he takes the lead in planning a weekend like this. I am so grateful that he does it. It's an awesome way for him to show me his love."

What Should We Talk About?

Many couples see the benefit of getting away for a day or a weekend, but are unsure of what they would do to fill all that time. One recommendation presented in this workbook is to talk through the questions presented by Tom Elliff (see page 144). And after you've asked the questions . . . listen. That's right, just listen to her response. This is not the time to get defensive or to explain why you do or don't do something. This is the time to hear your spouse's heart and let her share openly and honestly.

Also, on your getaway, take time to just enjoy the break from the speed of life. Take walks. Go sightseeing. Experience unrushed intimacy. Simply put, enjoy each other!

Having marriages and families that honor God and accomplish His purposes takes some effort. We need to take the necessary time to get away and talk about the important things of life. And when we do, great things can and will occur.

HAVING A VISION

FOR YOUR WORLD

GROUP DISCUSSION: GATHERING AT BASE CAMP

1. Dennis Rainey defines patriarchs as "men who reach down the steps, investing in the generations to come. They . . . realize their potential to have a lasting influence in their families and communities. [They are] generational connectors, generational influencers, and generational intercessors."

   In light of this definition, how was Brother Paul's dad fulfilling the function of a patriarch?

2. What are some things that keep men from acting as patriarchs?

3. Name some of the patriarchs you've known.

4. What kind of impact did they have on your life?

5. How do you define success?

6. How does this compare to some of the more common definitions of success?

7. Though he may have defined success differently as a young man, a true patriarch comes to know that there is no greater accomplishment in life than leaving a lasting spiritual legacy. What kind of mark do you hope to leave on this world?

From Your Time on the Trail (session 9)

8. How do you hope to do a better job of setting vision and direction for your family? (If you are single, share about the things you are doing now to prepare for a family.) (See question 1, page 143.)

9. What are you doing to help yourself follow through with setting vision? (See question 2, page 143.)

PERSONAL EXERCISE: LOGGING TIME ON THE TRAIL

DAY ONE

WHAT'S YOUR PATRIARCH ISSUE?

What kind of old man do you want to be? That question isn't meant to be disrespectful to the elderly. It's a sincere, though admittedly blunt, way of thinking about the future to which we're all heading. We're one step closer to "old age" (whatever that is) than we were yesterday, so today's a good day to start thinking about it. And planning for it.

A better question might be, "What lasting difference do you want your life to make?" Think outside yourself and beyond your lifespan. Your influence should outlive you. It should matter—*really* matter—that you were here. Wouldn't you love for this to be said about you: "Though he died, he still speaks" (Hebrews 11:4)?

+1. Describe the lasting difference (into your senior years and even beyond your death) that you hope your life will make. (You may want to refer all the way back to your answer to session 3, day 3, question 13.)

Think of this as your patriarch issue, the bull's-eye on the target of your life's purpose. As you think about it, and maybe even dream a little, remember: the course of your life is set by everyday choices. Today matters a great deal.

2. How do you think you're doing? Is your life on course with your patriarch issue?

☐ Generally, yes. I waver some, but get back on track quickly.

☐ I really haven't given it much thought.

- ☐ I used to have clear direction, but I've lost focus.

- ☐ I'm not on course, but I know what I need to do to get back on.

- ☐ I don't see the need to think about something so far in the future.

- ☐ Other:

BLESSED TO BLESS

You may be thinking, *I'm too young for all this patriarch stuff. That's for the older guys!* Then don't you find it interesting that Abram (later Abraham) wasn't even at halftime when God talked to him about it?

> Now the Lord said to Abram, "Go from your country and your kindred and your father's house to the land that I will show you. And I will make of you a great nation, and I will bless you and make your name great, so that you will be a blessing. I will bless those who bless you, and him who dishonors you I will curse, and in you all the families of the earth shall be blessed."
> —Genesis 12:1–3

But age isn't the most important issue here; God's purpose is. Essentially, God told Abram, *I blessed you so that you would be a blessing.* The sooner we realize that the things God pours into our lives are not for us alone, the closer we are to embracing His purpose for our lives. Like Abram, we have been blessed to be a blessing. We are not mere consumers of God's grace, we are conduits. God intends for His life to flow through us in ways that will bring His life to others.

THE GREAT HINDRANCE OF SIN

We cannot think about the impact our lives are making, or that we hope they will make, without addressing the issue of sin. Sin is the major obstacle we face in finding and fulfilling God's purpose, or in even caring about it. Perhaps sin has kept you from stepping up in your life, from becoming the man of God that you want and hope to be. Perhaps your forward progress hasn't lived up to your desire because you keep tripping over the same temptations and falling into the same sinful habits.

+3. Does the above description pertain to you? Is there a recurring sinful habit or pattern that has been holding you back from being the man God wants you to be?

☐ Yes   ☐ No

4. If you answered yes, describe the sinful habit you're struggling with and how it is affecting your spiritual growth. In other words, what would be true of you if this sin wasn't a part of your life?

5. What steps can you take to begin breaking the hold this sin has had on you?

Like so many things, breaking the power of sin requires outside help. For one thing, you *must* pray. Many times people will talk about the things that concern them but never really pray about them. As strange as this may sound, it is true. The point is, don't just talk about wanting to be free from sin's hold, pray!

Also, don't be reluctant to share your burden with another man or a small group of men who are trustworthy and leading a God-centered life. If men can't band together over one another's spiritual battles, then they're missing out on one of their most important assignments.

DAY TWO

You're on deck, one play away (in this case, one *day* away) from being up. Tomorrow you should complete the final lesson of this study. We hope that this experience has been—and will continue to be—a source of encouragement and direction.

Today's and tomorrow's lessons will be spent processing the information you have been putting into your Stepping Up Plan over the past several weeks. You have identified several areas of your life that need some degree of attention, and you've thought of steps you can take to advance in each of those areas. Now we want to help you whittle that information down even more—to one step—not with the intent of ignoring all the other steps you may need to take, but to encourage you. We believe that if you take one step immediately, you're more likely to take others.

+1. Before you begin processing further, you need to identify your "patriarch issue" (see question 1 in yesterday's lesson) and transfer it to the Patriarch step on your SUP.

YOUR STEPPING UP PLAN: PUTTING IT ALL TOGETHER

We've been using the acronym STEP as a simple way to outline the nature of a godly and courageous man. That man is concerned about:

> Standing firm
> Taking initiative
> Engaging with wisdom and grace
> Planning ahead and providing

This series has been all about helping a man grow in each of these areas of life so that he will lead and influence his family and his world. Men like this are needed. Very much needed.

Now it is time to put the finishing touches on your Stepping Up Plan so you can activate your plan and move forward, or shall we say . . . step up!

Starting with session 5, "Standing Firm," you began identifying certain areas of your life that need attention. You also determined next steps you should take; people who could help you; and habits, relationships, or circumstances that tend to erode your courage and commitment. The final thing we want to accomplish in this series is to help you determine *one* next step. Let's begin that process by looking at your "erosion issues."

EROSION

Of the various erosion issues we might identify, one should be of particular concern: patterns of sin. By this we mean the cycle of sin that many people can't seem to escape. Something sets them off, and they spiral downward into a prolonged season of selfishness and self-destruction. This often hurts the people who are closest to them and sometimes damages relationships beyond repair.

2. As you consider the various erosion issues you identified during this series, how many of them are related to a personal struggle with sin?

That you might struggle with sin comes as no surprise; the Bible tells us "there is no one who does not sin" (1 Kings 8:46). The difference-maker is in what you do in response to your sins and shortcomings. You can indulge them. Excuse them. Or confront them by agreeing with God, confessing, and repenting. And you can learn to be on the lookout for sin, knowing that certain situations have triggered a sinful reaction within you in the past.

3. Look again at your erosion issues. Do they point to a pattern of sinful thinking or behavior in your life? For example, if you've identified fear as an erosion issue, perhaps you need to check your heart for unbelief or pride. If certain people are an erosion issue, perhaps you are harboring anger, or even a desire for revenge. If shame is an erosion issue that is wearing you down, maybe you really need to come to grips with God's forgiveness and grace (suggestion: revisit session 4).

Be honest with yourself and before God. If needed, take some extended time to get quiet before God and ask Him to search your heart, knowing that He sees what you cannot. Remember, God's desire is not to beat you up, but to restore you.

4. What step can you take to deal with the sin pattern you identified?

DAY THREE

Congratulations! You've made it to the last day of this series. There's only one thing left for you to do, and it will be true to the adage "last, but not least." Today you determine the next step you will take in answering the call to courageous manhood. As we said yesterday, there are other steps we hope you will take after this one, but you probably won't take those if you don't take this one. So . . .

1. Consider all of the following areas:

☐ Where do you need to stand firm?

☐ In what ways do you need to take initiative?

☐ How can you improve as a leader by engaging with wisdom and grace?

☐ What do you need to develop in order to become a better planner and provider?

☐ What step should you take to begin leading your family with vision?

☐ How should you deal with sin?

Which of these is the most important to you right now and needs your attention as soon as possible? Pray through this question, then check your answer in the list above.

2. Referring to your SUP, what step did you identify needing to take in the area identified in question 1 above? Transfer that step to the Next Step on your SUP.

3. Throughout this series you have identified a number of individuals whom you feel could help you in various ways, from the individual sessions and the 360 review. Over the course of the past several weeks you have narrowed your list down to a few and have placed their names on your SUP. Now it is time to decide: whom will you contact first? (You may have already determined this by your answer to the previous two questions.)

Who will you contact? _____

When: Give yourself a deadline: I will contact this person no later than _____/_____/_____.

Transfer the "Who" and "When" to your SUP.

If at all possible, we suggest having this conversation in person, because you are asking him to participate in your life on a very personal level. By the way, we commend you for taking this courageous step. And the other steps that will surely follow.

You're done with the paperwork but not the real work. So here's our last challenge . . .

FOLLOW THROUGH!

NOTES

Session 1

1. *Merriam-Webster Online*, s.v. "courage," accessed May 24, 2012, http://www.merriam
-webster.com/dictionary/courage.

2. Dennis Rainey, *Stepping Up* (Little Rock, AR: FamilyLife, 2011), 5.

3. William Arndt, Frederick W. Danker, and Walter Bauer, *A Greek-English Lexicon of the New Testament and Other Early Christian Literature*, 3rd ed. (Chicago: University of Chicago Press, 2000), 76.

4. Adapted from Ron L. Deal, *The Smart Stepdad: Steps to Help You Succeed* (Minneapolis, MN: Bethany House, 2011), 238.

5. "Top Ten Things Men Fear," FearOfStuff, accessed May 24, 2012, http://www.fearofstuff
.com/headline/top-10-things-men-fear/.

Session 3

1. Adapted from Dr. Albert Mohler, "The Marks of Manhood," *The Rebelution*, Sept. 2006, http://
www.therebelution.com/resources/marks_of_manhood.htm. Used by permission.

Session 4

1. Jerry Bridges, *The Discipline of Grace* (Colorado Springs: NavPress, 2006), 27.

Session 6

1. Mark Hamby, "Biographies," Lamplighter Ministries International, http://www
.lamplighterpublishing.com/products.asp?dept=276.

Session 7

1. Yahoo! HotJobs annual job-satisfaction survey, cited in "Top 10 Qualities of a Good Boss," RISMedia, January 10, 2008, http://rismedia.com/2008-01-09/top-10-qualities-of-a-good
-boss/.

2. Adapted from Isaac Asimov, *Isaac Asimov's Treasury of Humor* (New York: Houghton Mifflin, 1971), 37–38.

3. "Lead Me" by Matt Hammitt, Chris Rohman & Jason Ingram © Birdwing Music/Toledo Tomorrow Music/1012 Rosedale Music/Sony ATV Cross Keys Publishing (ASCAP).

Solon and the Athenian Dilemma

1. Carl J. Richard, *Twelve Greeks and Romans who Changed the World* (New York: Fall River Press, 2006), 37.

Session 9

1. Neil Postman, *The Disappearance of Childhood* (New York: Vintage, 1994), xi.

2. Tom and Jeannie Elliff, "Ten Questions Every Husband Should Ask His Wife Annually," FamilyLife, accessed June 6, 2012, http://www.familylife.com/articles/topics/marriage
/staying-married/husbands/ten-questions-every-husband-should-ask-his-wife-annually.

3. Adapted from Rob Flood, "The Getaway Plan," FamilyLife, accessed June 4, 2012, http://
www.familylife.com/articles/topics/marriage/staying-married/communication/
the-getaway-plan.

STEPPING UP CONTRIBUTORS

Dan Allender

Dr. Dan B. Allender received his Master of Divinity from Westminster Theological Seminary and his PhD in Counseling Psychology from Michigan State University. Currently, he serves as Professor of Counseling at The Seattle School of Theology & Psychology. He travels and speaks extensively to present his unique perspective on sexual abuse recovery, love & forgiveness, worship, and other related topics. Dan is the author of *The Wounded Heart* and *The Healing Path* and has coauthored several books with Dr. Tremper Longman.

Voddie Baucham

Voddie Baucham Jr., DMin, is a husband, father, pastor, author, professor, conference speaker, and church planter. He currently serves as Dean of the Seminary at African Christian University in Lusaka, Zambia. He and his wife, Bridget, have nine children.

Bill Bennett

William J. Bennett, PhD, is one of America's most influential voices on cultural, political, and education issues. He is currently the chairman of Conservative Leaders for Education and serves on the advisory boards of Udacity and Viridis Learning, Inc. Bill has written and edited sixteen books, two of which, *The Book of Virtues* and *The Children's Book of Virtues*, rank among the most successful of the past decade. He and his wife, Elayne, have two sons and live in Maryland.

Matt Chandler

Matt serves as lead pastor of The Village Church in Highland Village, Texas. He is also involved in church planting, both locally and internationally, through The Village and other partnerships. He is married to Lauren and they have three children.

Tony Dungy

Tony is a former professional football player and retired coach for the Indianapolis Colts. He became the first African-American coach to win a Super Bowl in 2007. In January 2009, Tony announced his retirement from the Colts, ending a thirty-one-year NFL career. He has served as a speaker for the Fellowship of Christian Athletes and Athletes in Action among many other charitable and faith-based organizations. He and his wife, Lauren, have seven children.

Chuck Farneth

Chuck is the director of OutdoorLegacy, a Christian ministry that equips men with a biblical understanding of manhood, spurring them to invest themselves in the lives of their sons and daughters. Chuck is the 2001 ESPN Great Outdoor Games gold medalist in flyfishing. He and his wife, Sherry, live in Heber Springs, Arkansas.

Tim Grissom

Tim is a writer living in Little Rock, Arkansas, where he also serves as senior editor for FamilyLife Publishing. He is the author of numerous articles, has contributed to several books, and is the coauthor of the best-selling book, *Seeking Him*. Tim loves to help people understand how deeply the Bible speaks to the issues of life and to encourage them to find their rest in God.

Greg Gunn

Greg has owned his own financial-services business for twenty-two years and has always worked with families helping them focus on their personal finances. Now, through Family Vision Ministry, which he founded with Mark Naylor, he can impact families with a message to pass on for generations to come. Their mission statement is, "To see each successive generation, of every family, live more fully for God." He and his wife, Rhonda, have seven children.

Matt Hammitt

Matt is a singer-songwriter and a founding member of the band Sanctus Real, a Grammy-nominated and Dove Award-winning Christian group. Matt and is wife, Sarah, recently launched LEAD ME LIVE Events, conferences on men and marriage, and he is host and producer of "Lead Me Lifecast," an audio podcast on faith, family, marriage, and manhood. Sarah and Matt have three children.

Gregg Harris

Gregg serves as a teaching elder at Gresham Household of Faith in Oregon. He is internationally known as a pioneer advocate in the Christian home-schooling movement and has authored a best-selling book, *The Christian Home School*. Gregg and his late wife, Sono, have seven children.

Joshua Harris

God has graciously allowed Joshua to write five books, including *I Kissed Dating Goodbye*, *Dug Down Deep: Building Your Life on Truths That Last*, and his latest, *Humble Orthodoxy: Holding the Truth High Without Putting People Down*. He is the former pastor of Covenant Life Church in Gaithersburg, Maryland. He and his wife, Shannon, have three children.

Robert Lewis

Robert Lewis, DMin, is the founder of Men's Fraternity. He is passionate about helping men discover the biblical principles of authentic manhood. He has authored a number of books including *Raising a Modern-Day Knight* and *Rocking the Roles: Building a Win-Win Marriage*. Robert and his wife, Sherard, have four grown children.

Crawford Loritts

Dr. Crawford Loritts is the senior pastor of Fellowship Bible Church in Roswell, Georgia, the daily host of the radio program "Living a Legacy," an internationally known Bible teacher, and the author of several books including *A Passionate Commitment*, *Leadership as an Identity*, and *Never Walk Away*. Crawford and his bride, Karen, have been married since 1971. They have four grown children and ten grandchildren.

James MacDonald

James MacDonald, DMin, is the senior pastor of the Harvest Bible Chapel. His broadcast ministry *Walk in the Word* reaches more than three million people weekly. James's vision is that God will use him to plant 1,000 churches in his lifetime. He and his wife, Kathy, live in Illinois and have three grown children and five grandsons.

John Majors

John has served with FamilyLife since 2000. He has helped create key resources like The Art of Marriage® and Passport2Purity®. He also helped develop and served as audio host for Passport2Identity™ and authored *True Identity*. John and his wife, Julie, are Weekend to Remember® speakers and have three children.

Eric Metaxas

Eric has written for Veggie Tales, Chuck Colson, and *The New York Times* in his eclectic career. He is a best-selling author whose biographies, children's books, and works of popular apologetics have been translated into numerous languages. Eric's book *Bonhoeffer: Pastor, Martyr, Prophet, Spy* was on the *New York Times* Best Seller List. His biography *Amazing Grace: William Wilberforce and the Heroic Campaign to End Slavery* was the official companion book for the feature film *Amazing Grace*. Eric lives in Manhattan, with his wife and daughter.

David Naugle

David K. Naugle, PhD, ThD, is chair of the philosophy department at Dallas Baptist University where he has worked for twenty years. He also serves as a Fellow for the Wilberforce Forum, the Christian worldview think tank sponsored by Prison Fellowship near Washington, DC. *Reordered Love, Reordered Lives: Learning the Deep Meaning of Happiness* is Dr. Naugle's latest book. He and his wife, Deemie, live in Duncanville, Texas.

Chris Plekenpol

Chris is the senior pastor of Wells Branch Community Church in Austin, Texas. He graduated from the United States Military Academy at West Point and spent seven years in the United States Army. He served in South Korea and Iraq. While in Iraq, Chris wrote *Faith in the Fog of War Vol. I and II*. After resigning from the Army, he graduated from Dallas Theological Seminary. Chris is married to Adrienne and they have two sons.

Dennis Rainey

Dennis is the president and CEO of FamilyLife, a ministry of Campus Crusade for Christ, and the cohost of the nationally syndicated *FamilyLife Today*® radio program. He has authored or coauthored more than two dozen books including *Stepping Up: A Call to Courageous Manhood*. Dennis has spoken at numerous Weekend to Remember® marriage getaways across the United States and internationally. Dennis and his wife, Barbara, have six children and numerous grandchildren.

Rob Rienow

Rob married Amy in 1994 and they have been blessed with six children. He served as youth and family pastor at Wheaton Bible Church for eighteen years, and is now part of a church planting team in the Chicago area. God led Rob and Amy to launch Visionary Family Ministries, a ministry to inspire parents and grandparents to disciple their children, help couples create mission-driven marriages, and equip churches to build Bible-driven ministries. Their mission is to build the church through a global reformation of family discipleship.

Dewayne Washington

Dewayne is the senior pastor of the Love Church in downtown Fort Worth, Texas. He had a vision to reach young men in his community who were struggling to find success in life. Dewayne developed a curriculum with his peers which led to the start up of Gentlemen's Society where young men are trained through mentorship. He has seen gang members transformed into college-bound young men. Dewayne is also a musician, author, speaker, counselor, and life coach. He is married and has four children.

Stu Weber

Stu served as a Green Beret in Vietnam. It was there that he committed himself to a lifetime of vocational ministry. He and his wife, Linda, later joined a small group of friends in founding Good Shepherd Community Church near Portland, Oregon. Stu is much in demand as an international speaker, and he is the author of several books, including *Tender Warrior, Four Pillars of a Man's Heart, All the King's Men,* and *Along the Road to Manhood.* The Webers have three sons and ten grandchildren.

Byron Yawn

Byron is the senior pastor of Community Bible Church in Nashville, Tennessee. Previously, as an associate pastor, Byron was assigned the responsibility of the men's ministry where he discovered men's ministry was central to the church's mission. Byron and his wife, Robin, have three children.

RECOMMENDED RESOURCES

DATING

Harris, Joshua. *I Kissed Dating Goodbye.* Colorado Springs: Multnomah Books, 2003.

Jones, Debby, and Jackie Kendall. *Lady in Waiting: Developing Your Love Relationships.* Shippensburg, PA: Destiny Image, 1995.

PREMARRIAGE

Boehi, David, Brent Nelson, Jeff Schulte, and Lloyd Shadrach. *Preparing for Marriage.* Ventura, CA: Gospel Light, 1997.

Köstenberger, Andreas J., with David W. Jones. *God, Marriage, and Family: Rebuilding the Biblical Foundation.* Wheaton, IL: Crossway, 2010.

Lewis, Robert, and William Hendricks. *Rocking the Roles: Building a Win-Win Marriage.* Colorado Springs: NavPress, 1991.

MARRIAGE

Rainey, Dennis, and Barbara Rainey. *Staying Close: Stopping the Natural Drift Toward Isolation in Marriage.* Nashville: Thomas Nelson, 1989.

Harvey, Dave. *When Sinners Say "I DO": Discovering the Power of the Gospel for Marriage.* Wapwallopen, PA: Shepherd Press, 2010.

Thomas, Gary. *Sacred Marriage: What If God Designed Marriage to Make Us Holy More Than to Make Us Happy?* Grand Rapids, MI: Zondervan, 2002.

PARENTING

Tripp, Tedd. *Shepherding a Child's Heart.* Wapwallopen, PA: Shepherd Press, 2005.

Plowman, Ginger. *Don't Make Me Count to Three.* Wapwallopen, PA: Shepherd Press, 2004.

Farley, William. *Gospel-Powered Parenting: How the Gospel Shapes and Transforms Parenting.* Phillipsburg, NJ: P & R Publishing, 2009.

Rainey, Dennis. *Aggressive Girls, Clueless Boys.* Little Rock, AR: FamilyLife Publishing, 2012.

—. *Interviewing Your Daughter's Date.* Little Rock, AR: FamilyLife Publishing, 2012.

Rainey, Dennis, and Barbara Rainey. Passport2Purity® Getaway Kit. Little Rock, AR: FamilyLife Publishing, 2012.

Lewis, Robert. *Raising a Modern-Day Knight: A Father's Role in Guiding His Son to Authentic Manhood.* Carol Stream, IL: Tyndale House, 2007.

STEPFAMILIES

Deal, Ron L. *The Smart Stepdad*. Ada, MI: Bethany House, 2011.

—. *The Smart Stepfamily*. Ada, MI: Bethany House, 2006.

—. *The Smart Stepfamily* DVD: Small Group Resource. Ada, MI: Bethany House, 2010.

COUPLES IN CRISIS

Grissom, Steve, and Cheryl Grissom. Choosing Wisely Before You Divorce Kit. Wake Forest, NC: Church Initiative, 1996.

Kenworthy, George. *Before the Last Resort*. Little Rock, AR: FamilyLife, 2008.

Piper, John. *This Momentary Marriage: A Parable of Permanence*. Wheaton, IL: Crossway, 2009.

MEN AND MANHOOD

Jenkins, Jerry. *Hedges: Loving Your Marriage Enough to Protect It*. Wheaton, IL: Crossway, 2005.

Lepine, Bob. *The Christian Husband: God's Job Description for a Man's Most Challenging Assignment*. Ventura, CA: Regal, 2009.

Bennett, William. *The Book of Man: Readings on the Path to Manhood*. Nashville: Thomas Nelson, 2011.

Weber, Stu. *Tender Warrior: Every Man's Purpose, Every Woman's Dream, Every Child's Hope*. Colorado Springs: Multnomah Books, 2006.

SPIRITUAL GROWTH

Hughes, R. Kent. *Disciplines of a Godly Man*. Wheaton, IL: Crossway, 2006.

Whitney, Donald S. *Spiritual Disciplines for the Christian Life*. Colorado Springs: NavPress, 1997.

PORNOGRAPHY

Harris, Joshua. *Sex Isn't the Problem, (Lust Is): Sexual Purity in a Lust-Saturated World*. Colorado Springs: Multnomah Books, 2003.

Schaumburg, Harry. *Undefiled: Redemption From Sexual Sin, Restoration For Broken Relationships*. Chicago: Moody, 2009.

INTIMACY

Leman, Kevin. *Sheet Music: Uncovering the Secrets of Sexual Intimacy in Marriage*. Carol Stream, IL: Tyndale House, 2003.

Rainey, Dennis, and Barbara Rainey. *Rekindling the Romance*. Nashville: Thomas Nelson, 2007.

IDEAS FOR A NEXT STEP

FOR YOURSELF

- Read *Stepping Up: A Call to Courageous Manhood.*

- Join an accountability group or find a mentor who models biblical manhood.

- Listen to the *FamilyLife Today®* **radio broadcast**—daily encouragement from a biblical perspective.

WITH YOUR SON OR GRANDSON

- Take your teen/young adult son or grandson through **Stepping Up**. Learn more at FamilyLife.com/SteppingUp.

- Schedule a **Passport2Purity®** or **Passport2Identity®** weekend with your son.

WITH YOUR WIFE

- Connect with your spouse at a **Weekend to Remember®** **marriage getaway**. Find dates and locations at FamilyLife.com/weekendtoremember.

AT YOUR CHURCH

- Host **The Art of Marriage® video event.** Discover God's design for marriage at this one-and-a-half-day event.

- Lead a group study on marriage or parenting using **The Art of Marriage® Connect group studies for couples**, the **Homebuilders Parenting Series®**, or **Marriage Oneness video series.**

- Build into the lives of other men or make marriages and families stronger. Contact our coaching team for a no commitment, free consultation:
  Visit FamilyLife.com/SteppingUp/get-help
  Call 1-800-FL-TODAY.
  E-mail MinistryAdvisor@FamilyLife.com.

"Our marriage is blossoming into something incredible."

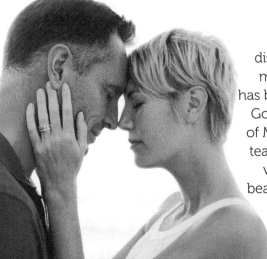

Learn what 750,000 people have discovered about enjoying a better marriage. For 40 years, FamilyLife® has been helping couples understand God's plan for relationships. The Art of Marriage® weaves together expert teaching, real-life stories, humorous vignettes and more to portray the beauty of God's design for marriage.

A boy without a father is like an explorer without a map

The Art of Marriage Video Event Kit

The perfect kickoff for your marriage ministry or an impactful weekend event for couples. Six engaging video sessions (55–60 minutes each) are interspersed with couple's projects that facilitate one-on-one discussions.

The Small-Group Series

Dive deep into God's design for marriage with couples over six weeks. Shorter video sessions (30 minutes), along with group discussion questions and date night ideas make this series ideal for a Sunday school or similar small-group setting.

To learn more, visit FamilyLife.com/ theartofmarriage.

FAMILYLIFE® presents

the art of **marriage**®

FAMILYLIFE® presents

weekend to
remember

GREAT MARRIAGES

DON'T JUST

happen.

Weekend to Remember is a two-and-a-half day weekend getaway that equips couples with practical tools and resources. Don't just survive, discover a marriage that THRIVES!

SAVE $100 per couple.

Go to WeekendtoRemember.com or call 1-800-FL-TODAY and use group code FLPFRIENDS.

About FamilyLife®

At FamilyLife we understand how good marriages and home life can be. And how challenging. That's why we work to provide tools and events that will help you build on a solid foundation, repair what has been broken, or reclaim what has been lost—all from a biblical perspective. Our books and resources offer practical, proven solutions to support you after that late-night argument with the kids, in the midst of a crushing confession, or when you simply need a new date-night idea. You'll find help for every stage of the journey, from pre-wedding jitters to the empty nest years and beyond.

Through each ministry offering, including Weekend to Remember®, Stepping Up®, The Art of Marriage®, and *FamilyLife Today*® radio broadcasts, FamilyLife shares biblical designs to help all kinds of families stay together—and value their togetherness—no matter what the future holds.

FamilyLife is a donor-supported ministry. We rely on friends like you—who recognize the critical role of the family—to help us reach even more marriages and homes.

Would you consider joining us in our mission? Please visit **FamilyLife.com/GetInvolved** to see the many ways you can partner with FamilyLife to help families across America and throughout the world. Thank you.

f facebook.com/familylifeministry   @FamilyLifeOrg

WAY TO STEP UP!

We are so glad you made the time for this Stepping Up® video series. We hope it has already had a profound impact on you. **But this is just the beginning.**

In addition to the recommended next steps outlined on page 168 of this workbook, we'd also like to offer you exclusive access to more tools to help you strengthen your walk with God.

Visit FamilyLife.com/SteppingUp where you can:

- Download the *Stepping Up: A Call to Courageous Manhood* e-book.
- Download free prayer cards to help pray for your family.
- Watch streaming video of all Stepping Up video series sessions.

To get these special offers and more, visit FamilyLife.com/SteppingUp

 Facebook.com/mensteppingup   YouTube.com/MenSteppingUp